SCRABBLE™ PUZZLES BOOK 1

Published by Collins
An imprint of HarperCollinsPublishers
Westerhill Road
Bishopbriggs
Glasgow G64 2QT
www.harpercollins.co.uk

HarperCollins*Publishers*
Macken House, 39/40 Mayor Street Upper
Dublin1, D01 C9W8, Ireland

All puzzles supplied by Clarity Media Ltd

First published in 2022

ISBN 978-0-00-852396-1

10 9 8 7 6 5 4 3 2

A catalogue record for this book is available from the British Library

Printed and bound in the UK using 100% renewable electricity at CPI Group (UK) Ltd

Collins

SCRABBLE™ PUZZLES

BOOK 1

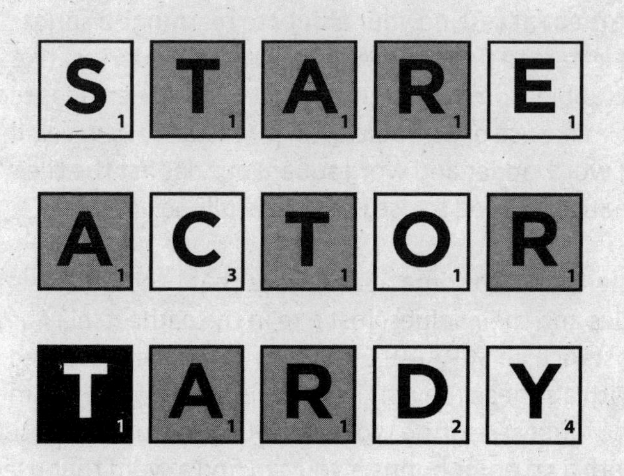

Introduction

Welcome to SCRABBLE™ PUZZLES: Book 1. This book contains a large range of 18 different word puzzles, so if you love Scrabble you're sure to find lots to enjoy in these pages. Some of the puzzles are short and will be relatively quick to solve, whilst others will present more of a challenge.

In addition to several common types of word puzzle such as wordsearches and word wheels, this book contains a range of anagram-based puzzles that will be great at testing your ability to rearrange a series of letters to find the longest word available, just like in Scrabble. Some other puzzle types have been adapted to make use of Scrabble tiles, for instance new versions of word ladder and word square puzzles list the tiles that you'll need to use to successfully solve them.

There are also some puzzle types that use Scrabble tiles and their values, just like in the game itself. For instance, in SCRABBLE™ Score you will be presented with a series of seven tiles and be tasked with finding the highest-scoring word that you can from those tiles, with a 50 point bonus if you can find a word that uses all seven letters. SCRABBLE™ Soup puzzles combine Scrabble tiles and their values with a wordsearch puzzle grid, and you must find the highest-scoring word you can hiding in the grid of letters.

Instructions are included each time a puzzle type occurs, and solutions are included at the back of the book so you can easily check your answers or get a helping hand if you get stuck with any of the challenges inside these pages. The individual solution words can be found in the Scrabble dictionary.

For your reference, here are the values for each Scrabble tile:

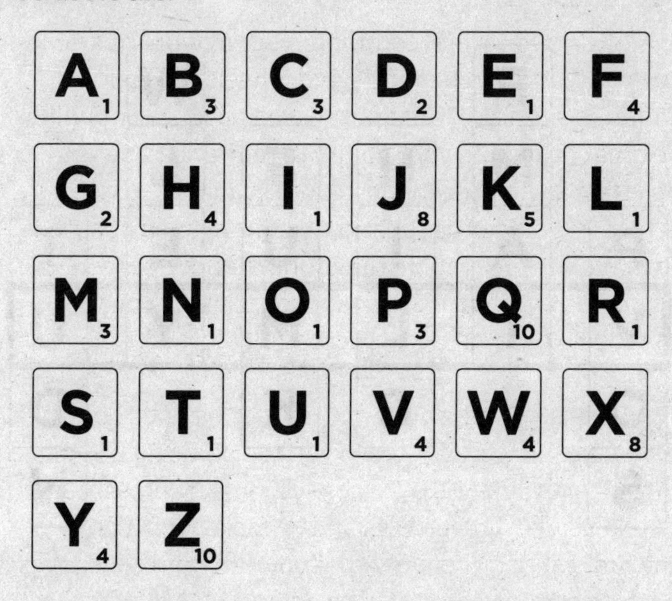

We hope you enjoy solving the puzzles in this book, and find them an enjoyable challenge that complements your games of Scrabble and the anagram-finding skills you have developed whilst playing the game.

Word Slider

Move each of the sliders up and down in order to form six-letter words in the middle row. Can you find five-or-more words?

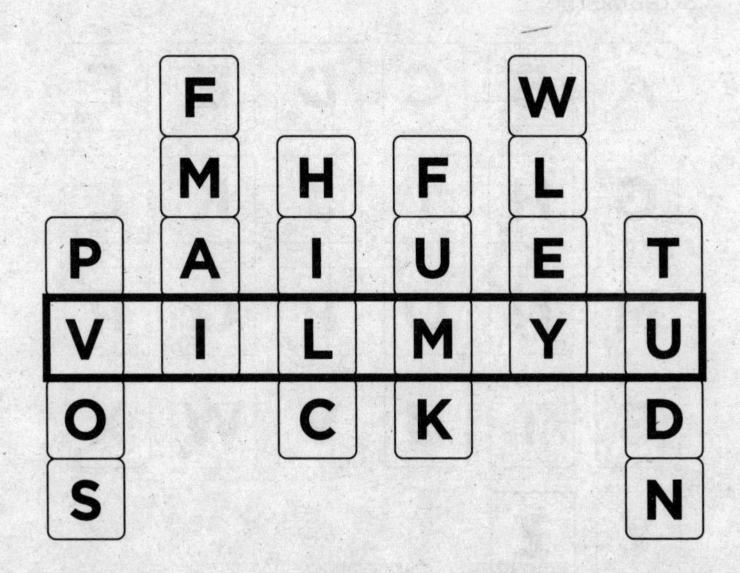

SCRABBLE™ Word

Can you guess the SCRABBLE™ Word? It is a word found in the Scrabble dictionary that does not repeat any letters. In each of the guesses below, a white background means the letter does not appear in the answer word. A black background means a letter is both found in the word and is in the correct position, whilst a grey background means a letter is found in the answer word, but in a different position.

Value of solution tiles: 8 points

Seven Letters

A word composed of seven different letters has been created using Scrabble tiles. Can you answer the clues below to work out what that word is? Numbers indicate the position of each letter in the answer word.

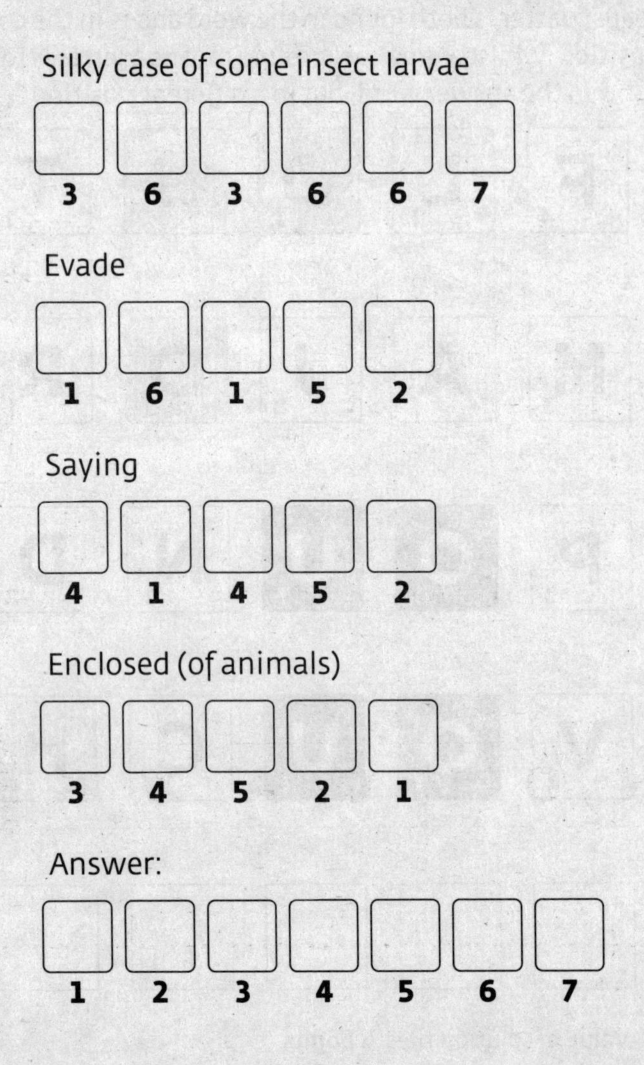

SCRABBLE™ Score

Make the highest score you can from each of the letter racks below. Add 50 points for a seven-letter word.

B3 A1 O1 D2 N1 A1 N1 — TRIPLE WORD SCORE

....

S1 C3 D2 T1 L1 O1 K5 — TRIPLE WORD SCORE

....

N1 O1 L1 Q10 A1 X8 K5 — DOUBLE SCORE ON 1ST LETTER

....

Wordsearch

Can you find all of these fabrics from the Scrabble wordlist in the grid below? Words may appear horizontally, vertically or diagonally in either a forwards or backwards direction.

P	M	M	O	L	E	S	K	I	N	B	J	V	M
L	Z	T	W	H	X	A	B	E	D	E	U	S	T
H	E	M	N	P	T	D	Z	H	B	C	G	Q	E
M	A	A	E	P	E	A	M	Z	H	G	F	C	V
J	I	N	T	E	I	U	P	E	W	L	Q	F	L
N	R	N	W	H	S	Q	E	A	V	K	S	G	E
I	A	T	I	L	E	S	L	O	B	M	F	I	V
L	I	I	I	T	E	R	E	Q	U	I	L	N	L
P	N	N	H	C	A	L	N	F	R	N	L	G	I
O	T	S	L	V	A	S	N	Y	L	E	I	H	G
P	E	O	G	C	C	J	A	N	A	D	W	A	K
M	T	X	E	B	Z	T	L	Z	P	Q	T	M	W
H	Q	H	G	C	H	I	F	F	O	N	C	Z	G
B	R	O	C	A	D	E	X	P	J	L	T	P	E

BROCADE
BURLAP
CHEESECLOTH
CHIFFON
DENIM
FLANNEL
GINGHAM
LACE
LEATHER
MESH
MOLESKIN
MUSLIN
POPLIN
SATIN
SUEDE
TWEED
TWILL
VELVET

Give Me a Clue

Can you fill-in the blank tiles to create a word that solves each of the clues below?

Ruined

D _ _ _ R _ Y _ _

Small insect that destroys crops

_ E _ V _ _

Long song or poem

_ A _ L _ _

Herb

_ A _ J _ _ _ M

Anagrams

Can you find the word that can be made from the following letters?

DAARKVRA

....

Can you find the two words that can be made from the following letters?

NANDOYE

....

....

Can you find the three words that can be made from the following letters?

AIEMD

....

....

....

Themed Anagrams

Can you crack these anagrams relating to agriculture?

SLICK VOTE

....

RIGATONI MEN

....

SNIDE LEG

....

VEGAN SHIRT

....

Word Wheel

Find as many words of 4+ letters as you can, using the letters in the wheel. All words must use the central letter. One word will use all the letters in the wheel.

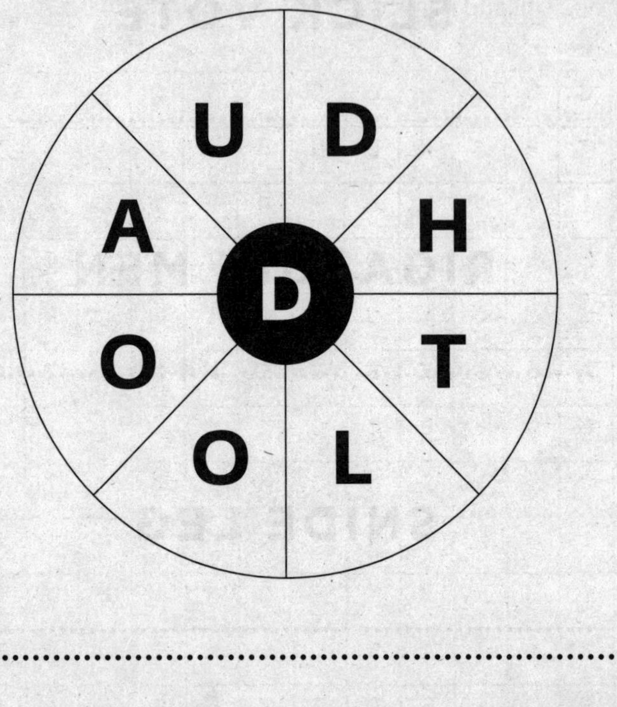

....

....

....

....

....

SCRABBLE™ Soup

Find the highest-scoring word you can in the grid of letters below by summing the values assigned to each letter tile in your word: for instance the word EXAMPLE would score 18 points. Words may appear horizontally, vertically or diagonally in the grid, and in either a forwards or backwards direction.

A 1	C 3	D 2	E 1	P 3	O 1	S 1	I 1	T 1	O 1	R 1	Y 4	D 2	O 1
H 4	T 1	A 1	S 1	K 5	E 1	D 2	L 1	S 1	G 2	A 1	I 1	Y 4	C 3
E 1	I 1	I 1	L 1	H 4	A 1	I 1	R 1	E 1	T 1	L 1	U 1	B 3	C 3
L 1	D 2	E 1	E 1	E 1	O 1	R 1	F 4	T 1	A 1	N 1	R 1	A 1	I 1
I 1	E 1	Y 4	G 2	Y 4	S 1	A 1	C 3	T 1	B 3	U 1	V 4	E 1	D 2
C 3	A 1	E 1	O 1	E 1	E 1	E 1	E 1	H 4	N 1	Q 10	Z 10	R 1	E 1
O 1	G 2	R 1	E 1	E 1	C 3	E 1	L 1	C 3	I 1	B 3	I 1	V 4	N 1
P 3	O 1	I 1	L 1	I 1	N 1	G 2	H 4	E 1	O 1	V 4	T 1	E 1	T 1
T 1	I 1	N 1	H 4	E 1	R 1	I 1	T 1	G 2	C 3	A 1	I 1	A 1	P 3
E 1	T 1	U 1	K 5	S 1	K 5	N 1	G 2	S 1	I 1	T 1	E 1	S 1	A 1
R 1	Z 10	A 1	I 1	R 1	S 1	L 1	S 1	A 1	R 1	U 1	I 1	T 1	T 1
S 1	E 1	O 1	I 1	E 1	E 1	R 1	H 4	E 1	E 1	E 1	T 1	N 1	U 1
B 3	C 3	R 1	I 1	T 1	I 1	C 3	I 1	S 1	M 3	I 1	T 1	S 1	G 2
Q 10	F 4	I 1	R 1	E 1	B 3	A 1	L 1	L 1	E 1	Z 10	R 1	M 3	R 1

Word Ladder

Use each of the tiles once to move from the word at the top of the ladder to the word at the bottom. You may only change one letter on each rung of the ladder, and must make a valid word on each rung. Use each of the Scrabble tiles once to do so.

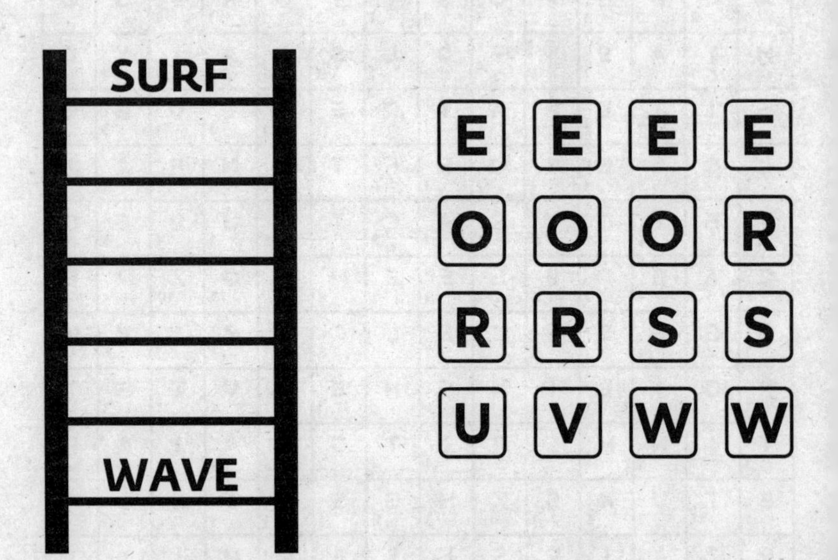

Star Letter

Find the word that can be made using every letter once, and the star letter twice.

Find the word that can be made using every letter once, and the star letter three times.

Consonant Crossword

Complete the crossword puzzle, in which all the vowels have already been placed. You must use each consonant tile listed once to fill the grid.

Word Splits

Can you combine the word segments
below to make three words?

ARY UND BO

....

VID DI END

....

VA BOU RD LE

....

Link Words

Find the word that can replace the question marks on each line to make two new words or phrases. Use each of the Scrabble tiles once to do so.

FAST ????? RECORD

FLAG ????? ROOM

WHIRL ???? SIDE

A A C F
F K L O
O P R S
T T

Missing Vowels

All the vowels have been removed from three words. Use each of the vowel tiles below once to reconstruct the words.

1) MCQ

2) VSG

3) TRRGN

A A A A
A E E I
O U

Word Square

Use the Scrabble tiles provided to fill the grid, so that the answer to each crossword clue appears in the corresponding row of the grid. Once complete, the same answer words will also appear in the columns.

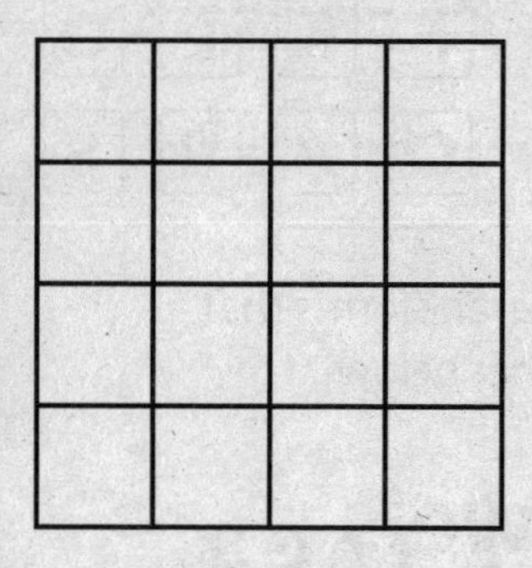

Light in shade

Jelly or culture medium

Molten rock

Time periods

A A E E

G L L P

R R S V

Unscramble

Can you unscramble the two dog breeds that have been mixed together below?

HANDBAG SCHEDULE

....

....

Can you unscramble the three landforms that have been mixed together below?

OBTAIN ROYAL TAGS

....

....

....

Word Slider

Move each of the sliders up and down in order to form six-letter words in the middle row. Can you find five-or-more words?

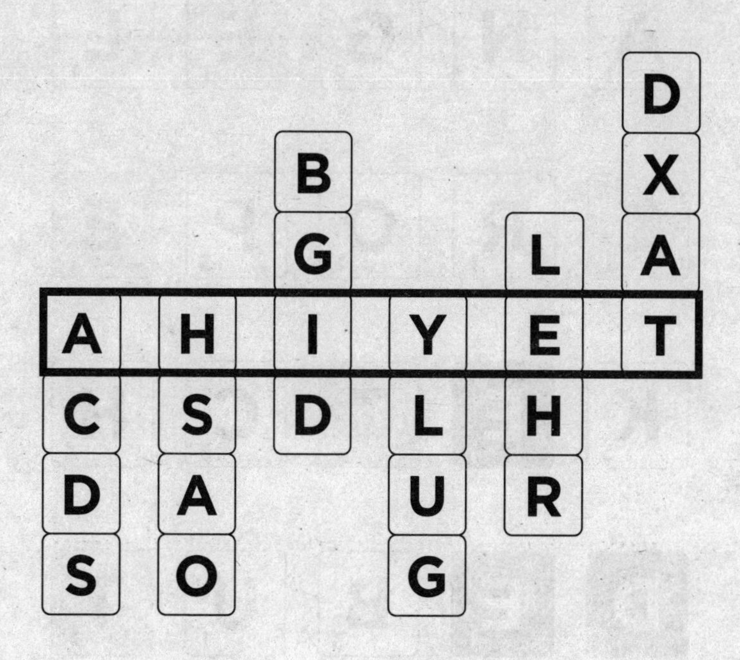

SCRABBLE™ Word

Can you guess the SCRABBLE™ Word? It is a word found in the Scrabble dictionary that does not repeat any letters. In each of the guesses below, a white background means the letter does not appear in the answer word. A black background means a letter is both found in the word and is in the correct position, whilst a grey background means a letter is found in the answer word, but in a different position.

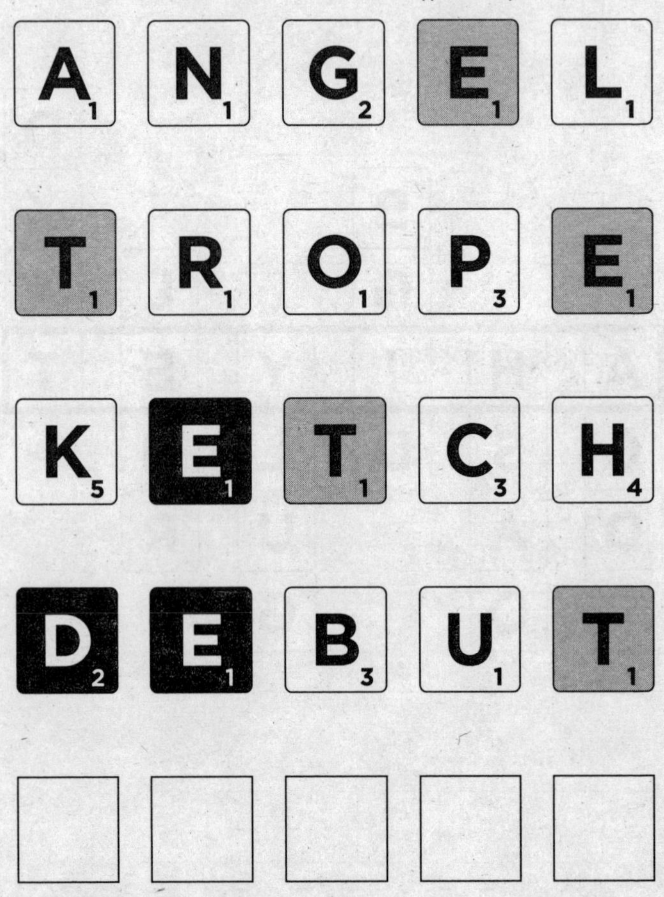

Value of solution tiles: 9 points

Seven Letters

A word composed of seven different letters has been created using Scrabble tiles. Can you answer the clues below to work out what that word is? Numbers indicate the position of each letter in the answer word.

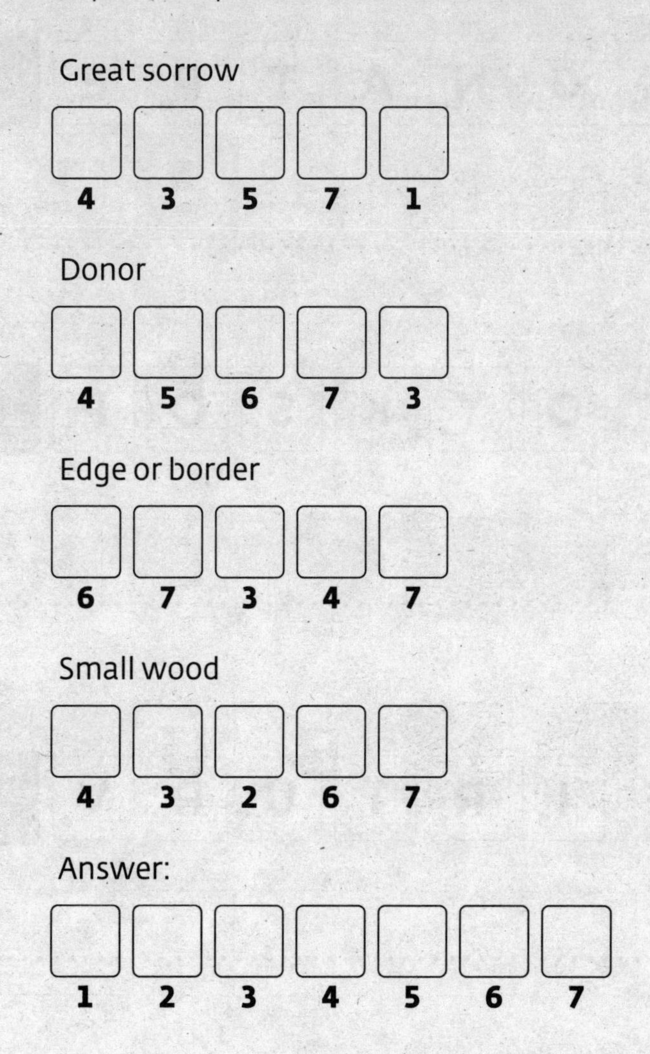

SCRABBLE™ Score

Make the highest score you can from each of the letter racks below. Add 50 points for a seven-letter word.

A 1 | G 2 | N 1 | A 1 | T 1 | P 3 | E 1 | DOUBLE WORD SCORE

....

T 1 | O 1 | Y 4 | K 5 | S 1 | O 1 | P 3 | DOUBLE SCORE ON 6TH LETTER

....

E 1 | I 1 | R 1 | T 1 | U 1 | R 1 | V 4 | TRIPLE WORD SCORE

....

Wordsearch

Can you find all of these sculpture-related words from the Scrabble wordlist in the grid below? Words may appear horizontally, vertically or diagonally in either a forwards or backwards direction.

E	N	O	T	S	P	A	O	S	A	A	H	Y	R
G	R	C	X	L	I	F	U	N	T	T	S	U	B
N	Q	I	N	Z	F	D	I	T	M	O	D	E	L
I	K	L	O	K	N	T	O	E	A	K	C	M	E
T	I	Y	O	A	A	C	V	S	C	L	H	M	T
S	H	R	S	P	A	O	Z	O	J	Y	I	G	I
A	U	C	Y	R	Q	A	R	I	L	X	S	M	N
C	N	A	R	V	S	M	X	C	F	T	E	Q	A
Y	X	E	E	L	B	R	A	M	S	J	L	J	R
R	T	A	S	S	E	M	B	L	A	G	E	Z	G
R	U	M	A	R	T	O	G	D	Z	J	L	U	K
U	M	G	R	I	L	O	E	U	T	A	T	S	I
L	T	T	V	R	O	T	P	L	U	C	S	X	K
X	C	J	W	N	A	Y	I	E	Z	N	O	R	B

ACRYLIC
ART
ASSEMBLAGE
BRONZE
BUST
CASTING
CHISEL
GRANITE
JADE
MARBLE
MODEL
PATINA
ROCK
SAND
SCULPTOR
SOAPSTONE
STATUE
TERRACOTTA

Give Me a Clue

Can you fill-in the blank tiles to create a word
that solves each of the clues below?

Long vehicle

_ I _ _ _ S _ _ E

Suitcases

B _ _ G _ _ _

Meeting plan

A _ _ _ _ A

Senior company figure

D _ _ _ C _ O _

Anagrams

Can you find the word that can be made from the following letters?

BRETTYA

....

Can you find the two words that can be made from the following letters?

IUCONTA

....

....

Can you find the three words that can be made from the following letters?

LABRYE

....

....

....

Themed Anagrams

Can you crack these anagrams relating to history?

TURNIP SCAM

....

OPEN CAVERN

....

HOT RAISIN

....

RICH CLONE

....

Word Wheel

Find as many words of 4+ letters as you can, using the letters in the wheel. All words must use the central letter. One word will use all the letters in the wheel.

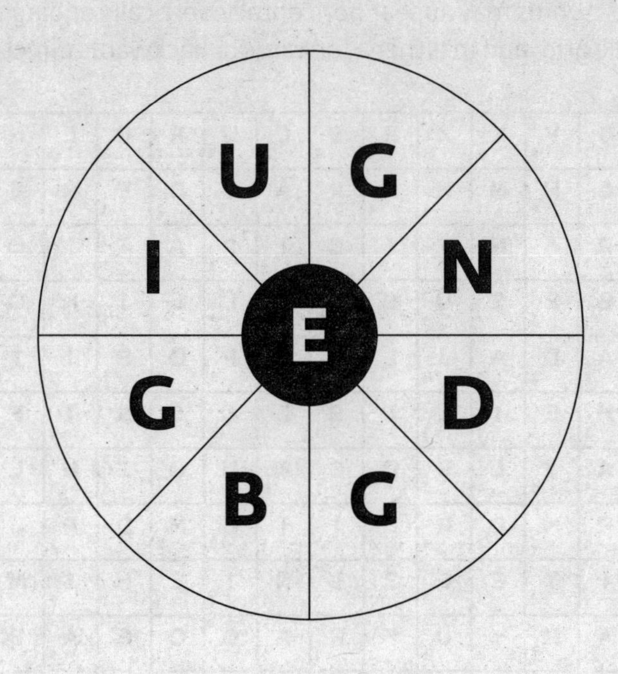

....

....

....

....

....

SCRABBLE™ Soup

Find the highest-scoring word you can in the grid of letters below by summing the values assigned to each letter tile in your word: for instance the word EXAMPLE would score 18 points. Words may appear horizontally, vertically or diagonally in the grid, and in either a forwards or backwards direction.

T 1	S 1	V 4	X 8	X 8	R 1	E 1	C 3	U 1	R 1	R 1	E 1	N 1	T 1
P 3	C 3	H 4	N 1	H 4	A 1	R 1	A 1	I 1	D 2	E 1	R 1	E 1	W 4
H 4	R 1	A 1	N 1	T 1	I 1	C 3	I 1	P 3	A 1	T 1	I 1	O 1	N 1
O 1	E 1	B 3	E 1	U 1	G 2	C 3	A 1	L 1	L 1	I 1	N 1	G 2	T 1
B 3	A 1	D 2	A 1	J 8	L 1	A 1	E 1	P 3	O 1	S 1	I 1	T 1	S 1
I 1	M 3	E 1	I 1	L 1	E 1	E 1	L 1	C 3	S 1	S 1	T 1	E 1	X 8
A 1	A 1	Y 4	L 1	S 1	D 2	C 3	K 5	U 1	O 1	E 1	N 1	L 1	L 1
S 1	R 1	M 3	D 2	R 1	P 3	I 1	T 1	C 3	M 3	D 2	P 3	U 1	S 1
R 1	I 1	T 1	E 1	E 1	Z 10	L 1	N 1	I 1	E 1	N 1	T 1	M 3	P 3
Y 4	A 1	M 3	V 4	U 1	F 4	R 1	A 1	G 2	O 1	E 1	A 1	B 3	E 1
O 1	Z 10	I 1	I 1	R 1	O 1	A 1	O 1	C 3	P 3	N 1	E 1	A 1	I 1
L 1	O 1	T 1	E 1	A 1	T 1	B 3	M 3	K 5	E 1	A 1	Y 4	G 2	K 5
V 4	E 1	J 8	E 1	I 1	N 1	P 3	A 1	E 1	B 3	L 1	M 3	O 1	I 1
E 1	I 1	B 3	U 1	S 1	P 3	I 1	R 1	I 1	T 1	S 1	E 1	H 4	R 1

Word Ladder

Use each of the tiles once to move from the word at the top of the ladder to the word at the bottom. You may only change one letter on each rung of the ladder, and must make a valid word on each rung. Use each of the Scrabble tiles once to do so.

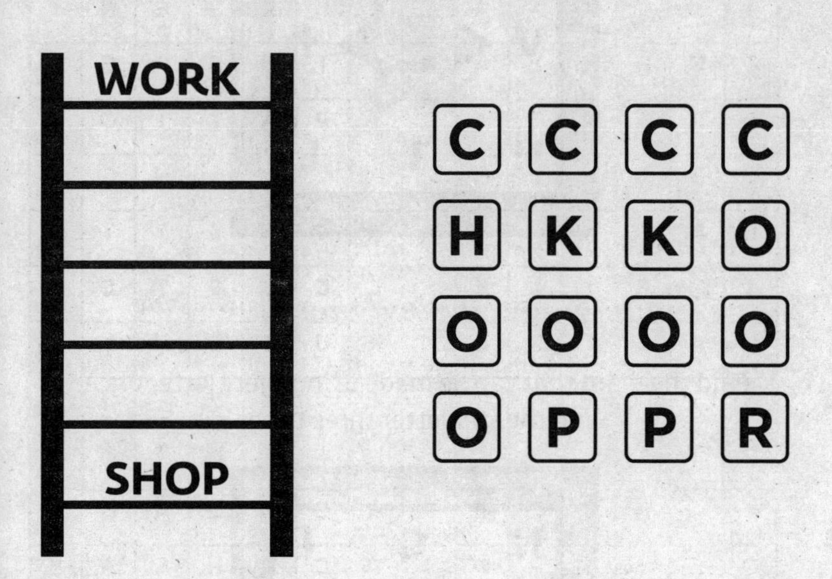

Star Letter

Find the word that can be made using every letter once, and the star letter twice.

....

Find the word that can be made using every letter once, and the star letter three times.

....

Consonant Crossword

Complete the crossword puzzle, in which all the vowels have already been placed. You must use each consonant tile listed once to fill the grid.

L L N N

P R S S

S T T W

Word Splits

Can you combine the word segments
below to make three words?

CA IN TE DI

....

ASI ON OCC

....

IE NCE PAT

....

Link Words

Find the word that can replace the question marks on each line to make two new words or phrases. Use each of the Scrabble tiles once to do so.

BLUE ????? HOPPER

SIDE ???? CASE

STOP ????? MAKER

A A C G
H H O R
S S S T
W W

Missing Vowels

All the vowels have been removed from three words. Use each of the vowel tiles below once to reconstruct the words.

1) RKSM

2) LLGL

3) CCMLT

A A A E
E E I I
O U U

Word Square

Use the Scrabble tiles provided to fill the grid, so that the answer to each crossword clue appears in the corresponding row of the grid. Once complete, the same answer words will also appear in the columns.

Money paid for a journey

Word ending a prayer

Tall grass

Finishes

E F M N

N R R S

Unscramble

Can you unscramble the two desserts that have been mixed together below?

WISE MINIBAR TOUR

....

....

Can you unscramble three types of fish that have been mixed together below?

NOTABLE SUIT HAUL

....

....

....

Word Slider

Move each of the sliders up and down in order to form six-letter words in the middle row. Can you find five-or-more words?

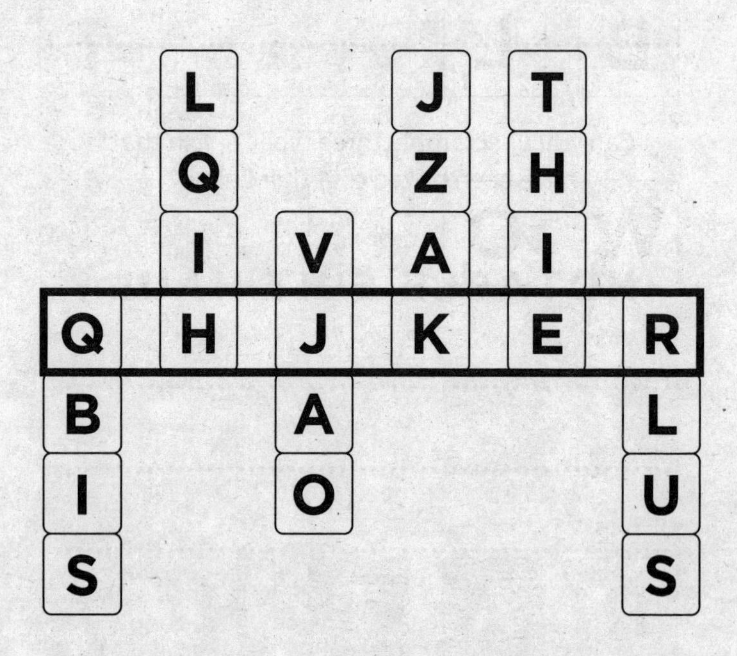

SCRABBLE™ Word

Can you guess the SCRABBLE™ Word? It is a word found in the Scrabble dictionary that does not repeat any letters. In each of the guesses below, a white background means the letter does not appear in the answer word. A black background means a letter is both found in the word and is in the correct position, whilst a grey background means a letter is found in the answer word, but in a different position.

Value of solution tiles: 8 points

Seven Letters

A word composed of seven different letters has been created using Scrabble tiles. Can you answer the clues below to work out what that word is? Numbers indicate the position of each letter in the answer word.

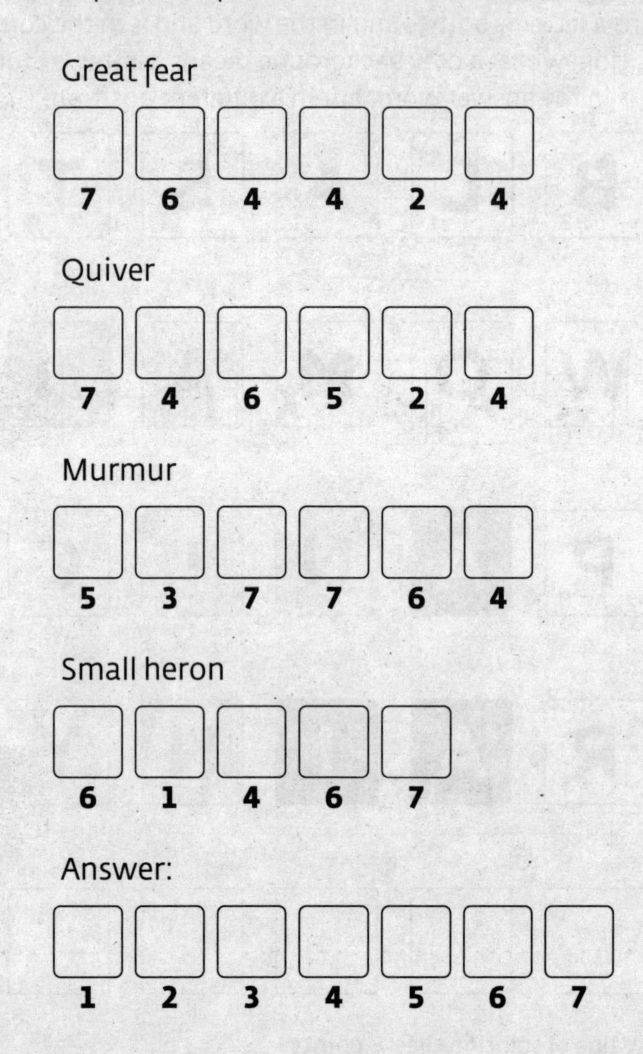

SCRABBLE™ Score

Make the highest score you can from each of the letter racks below. Add 50 points for a seven-letter word.

L	S	O	F	M	B	Y	TRIPLE SCORE ON 6TH LETTER
1	1	1	4	3	3	4	

M	X	A	I	X	M	K	TRIPLE SCORE ON 5TH LETTER
3	8	1	1	8	3	5	

V	C	H	Q	N	E	U	TRIPLE SCORE ON 1ST LETTER
4	3	4	10	1	1	1	

Wordsearch

Can you find all of these plants from the Scrabble wordlist in the grid below? Words may appear horizontally, vertically or diagonally in either a forwards or backwards direction.

V	R	C	K	L	F	Y	R	O	C	I	H	C	E
S	Y	P	L	J	A	S	M	I	N	E	V	A	V
A	R	E	P	B	M	V	I	C	D	X	D	L	O
N	R	Y	C	U	H	U	E	I	E	I	Z	U	L
D	E	O	H	N	F	Y	Q	N	H	D	L	P	G
W	B	W	F	L	I	C	S	C	D	E	A	O	X
O	R	E	L	T	O	U	R	S	D	E	L	R	O
R	A	D	E	D	R	O	Q	O	O	C	R	D	F
T	B	N	A	N	A	D	H	L	W	P	Q	W	V
V	X	U	B	V	T	P	U	S	V	O	Z	O	T
S	U	S	A	A	S	O	O	B	M	A	B	N	R
C	L	J	N	A	Q	Q	S	H	J	P	R	S	Z
I	Q	K	E	V	L	E	Z	A	H	P	I	S	I
A	G	C	E	N	O	R	D	A	M	Q	H	S	H

ASPHODEL
BAMBOO
BARBERRY
CEDAR
CHICORY
FLEABANE
FOXGLOVE
HAZEL
HYSSOP
JASMINE
LAVENDER
MADRONE
ORCHID
QUINCE
SANDWORT
SNOWDROP
SUNDEW
TARO

Give Me a Clue

Can you fill-in the blank tiles to create a word that solves each of the clues below?

Brochure

| | E | | F | | | |

Trick to attract publicity

| | I | | | | | K |

Of times long ago

| | E | | | | V | | L |

Spending plan

| B | | | G | | |

Anagrams

Can you find the word that can be made from the following letters?

ECNYMECL

....

Can you find the two words that can be made from the following letters?

BDEAETL

....

....

Can you find the three words that can be made from the following letters?

EPSCO

....

....

....

Themed Anagrams

Can you crack these anagrams relating to economics?

CURTAIL ICON

....

FAINT LION

....

EVENT MINTS

....

CONTAINS RAT

....

Word Wheel

Find as many words of 4+ letters as you can, using the letters in the wheel. All words must use the central letter. One word will use all the letters in the wheel.

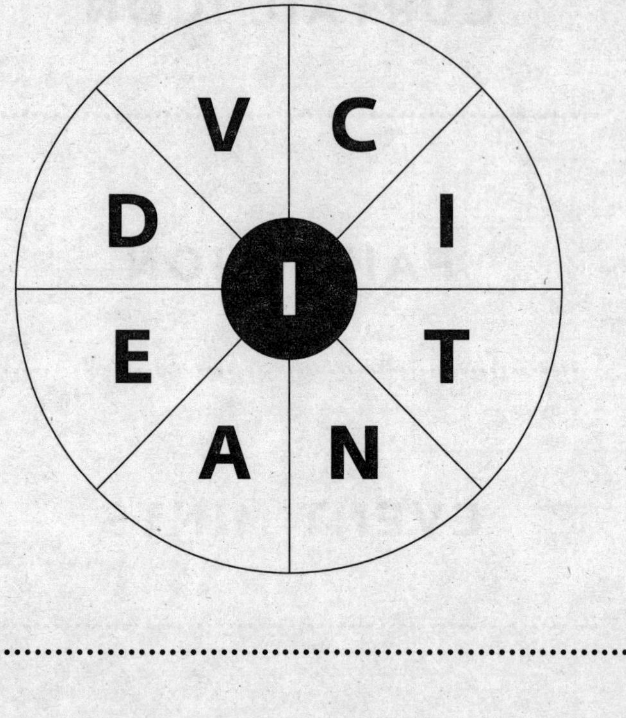

....

....

....

....

....

SCRABBLE™ Soup

Find the highest-scoring word you can in the grid of letters below by summing the values assigned to each letter tile in your word: for instance the word EXAMPLE would score 18 points. Words may appear horizontally, vertically or diagonally in the grid, and in either a forwards or backwards direction.

E 1	P 3	C 3	C 3	T 1	W 4	E 1	E 1	T 1	E 1	R 1	S 1	T 1	U 1
I 1	S 1	O 1	O 1	B 3	U 1	P 3	H 4	E 1	A 1	V 4	A 1	L 1	M 3
O 1	H 4	T 1	M 3	R 1	T 1	S 1	M 3	U 1	S 1	T 1	E 1	R 1	S 1
I 1	E 1	W 4	M 3	E 1	C 3	S 1	C 3	F 4	Q 10	R 1	L 1	Q 10	D 2
M 3	L 1	R 1	U 1	A 1	U 1	R 1	F 4	L 1	S 1	Z 10	U 1	C 3	O 1
M 3	T 1	E 1	T 1	D 2	R 1	F 4	R 1	H 4	O 1	A 1	O 1	H 4	Q 10
E 1	E 1	S 1	E 1	F 4	T 1	L 1	R 1	P 3	B 3	S 1	U 1	U 1	C 3
D 2	R 1	T 1	R 1	R 1	A 1	W 4	C 3	B 3	E 1	I 1	E 1	I 1	B 3
I 1	I 1	L 1	N 1	U 1	I 1	A 1	L 1	U 1	A 1	S 1	E 1	D 2	U 1
A 1	N 1	E 1	A 1	I 1	N 1	E 1	L 1	T 1	A 1	K 5	O 1	I 1	I 1
T 1	G 2	R 1	L 1	T 1	S 1	L 1	I 1	J 8	T 1	V 4	I 1	T 1	L 1
E 1	E 1	A 1	L 1	S 1	C 3	I 1	S 1	S 1	I 1	O 1	N 1	S 1	D 2
L 1	T 1	D 2	T 1	S 1	I 1	L 1	L 1	I 1	E 1	S 1	T 1	R 1	S 1
Y 4	S 1	A 1	G 2	R 1	E 1	E 1	D 2	C 3	E 1	S 1	W 4	X 8	Z 10

Word Ladder

Use each of the tiles once to move from the word at the top of the ladder to the word at the bottom. You may only change one letter on each rung of the ladder, and must make a valid word on each rung. Use each of the Scrabble tiles once to do so.

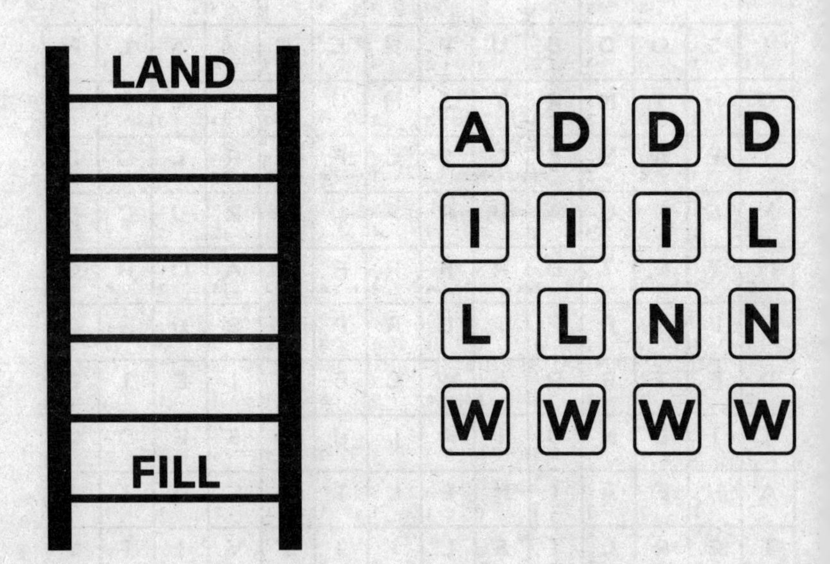

Star Letter

Find the word that can be made using every letter once, and the star letter twice.

Find the word that can be made using every letter once, and the star letter three times.

Consonant Crossword

Complete the crossword puzzle, in which all the vowels have already been placed. You must use each consonant tile listed once to fill the grid.

Word Splits

Can you combine the word segments below to make three words?

PA LEL RAL

....

HED SC ULE

....

URY TRE AS

....

Link Words

Find the word that can replace the question marks on each line to make two new words or phrases. Use each of the Scrabble tiles once to do so.

HORSE ???? COURSE

POLICE ????? SCHOOL

SPOT ????? LIST

A A C C
C E E E
H K R S
T T

Missing Vowels

All the vowels have been removed from three words. Use each of the vowel tiles below once to reconstruct the words.

1) CNMY

2) CJL

3) CLCM

A A E
E I O
O O U

Word Square

Use the Scrabble tiles provided to fill the grid, so that the answer to each crossword clue appears in the corresponding row of the grid. Once complete, the same answer words will also appear in the columns.

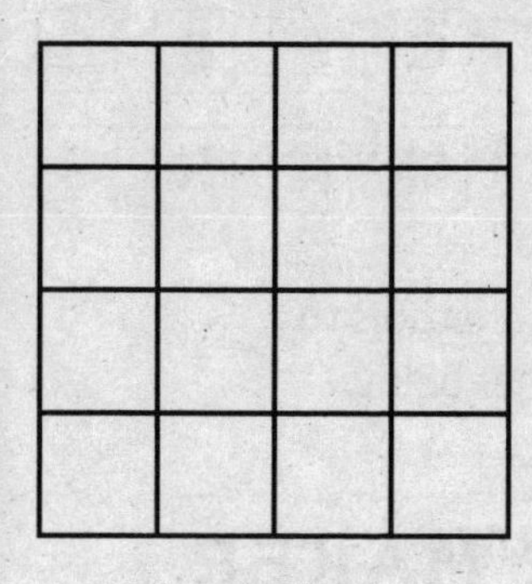

Social insects

Standard

A group of three

Type of air pollution

S S T T

Unscramble

Can you unscramble the two words that mean 'angry' that have been mixed together below?

AIRING OF GURUS

....

....

Can you unscramble the three tools that have been mixed together below?

CALM HAMPER MAKER

....

....

....

Word Slider

Move each of the sliders up and down in order to form six-letter words in the middle row. Can you find five-or-more words?

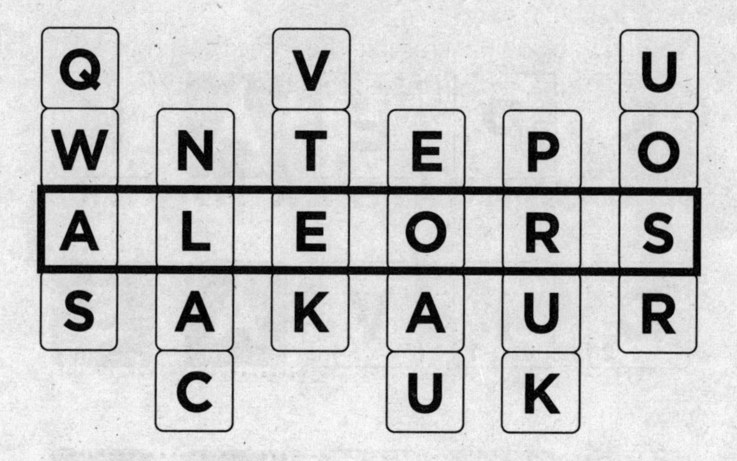

SCRABBLE™ Word

Can you guess the SCRABBLE™ Word? It is a word found in the Scrabble dictionary that does not repeat any letters. In each of the guesses below, a white background means the letter does not appear in the answer word. A black background means a letter is both found in the word and is in the correct position, whilst a grey background means a letter is found in the answer word, but in a different position.

Value of solution tiles: 7 points

Seven Letters

A word composed of seven different letters has been created using Scrabble tiles. Can you answer the clues below to work out what that word is? Numbers indicate the position of each letter in the answer word.

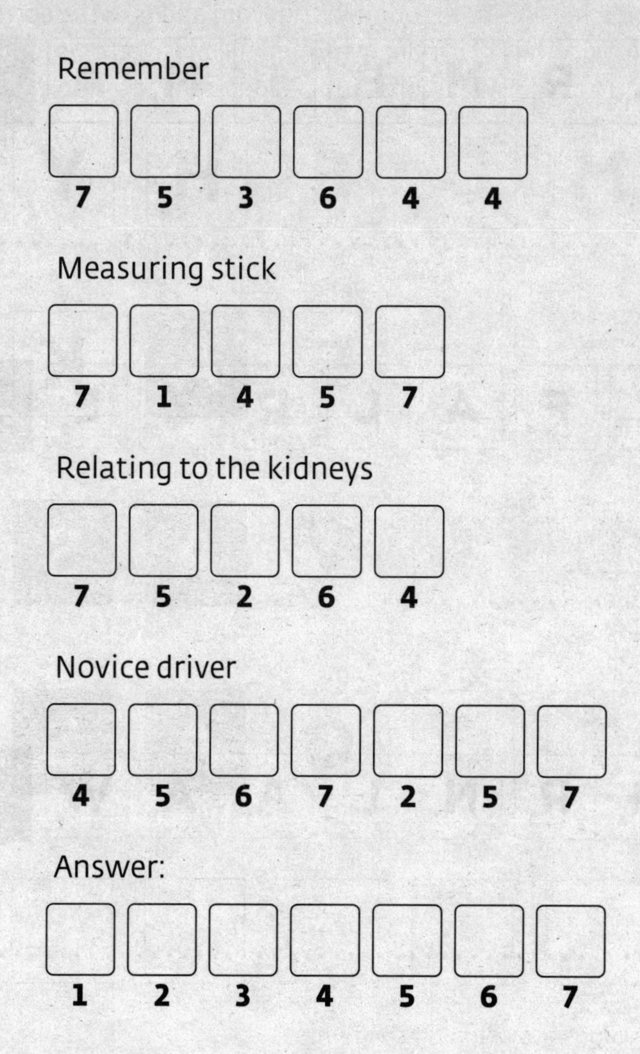

SCRABBLE™ Score

Make the highest score you can from each of the letter racks below. Add 50 points for a seven-letter word.

A[1] R[1] M[3] B[3] I[1] M[3] A[1] — DOUBLE WORD SCORE

Z[10] F[4] A[1] L[1] R[1] Z[10] E[1] — DOUBLE SCORE ON 3RD LETTER

H[4] R[1] N[1] L[1] A[1] A[1] W[4] — TRIPLE SCORE ON 6TH LETTER

Wordsearch

Can you find all of these birds from the Scrabble wordlist in the grid below? Words may appear horizontally, vertically or diagonally in either a forwards or backwards direction.

W	A	U	K	S	R	E	L	B	R	A	W	B	Y
Z	W	O	L	L	A	W	S	B	X	P	U	P	B
R	D	E	S	U	O	R	G	K	L	S	P	R	P
C	A	S	N	R	E	T	T	E	T	H	D	M	W
M	R	J	M	L	M	H	R	A	E	G	R	Y	C
P	A	Z	T	Q	L	T	R	A	K	I	I	N	F
A	C	K	P	H	E	D	S	Z	B	Y	B	E	R
R	A	J	B	P	G	A	B	X	N	W	N	R	A
T	R	E	B	S	N	I	D	E	A	Y	U	W	V
R	A	C	I	T	Q	D	N	T	R	M	S	J	I
I	C	B	T	T	E	E	K	A	R	A	P	X	X
D	I	J	A	C	K	D	A	W	K	R	A	T	M
G	P	L	O	V	E	R	D	V	O	G	R	I	D
E	H	S	Z	O	S	P	A	R	R	O	W	D	G

BUSTARD
CARACARA
GROUSE
IBIS
JACKDAW
NIGHTJAR
PARAKEET
PARTRIDGE
PETREL
PHEASANT
PLOVER
SKUA
SPARROW
SUNBIRD
SWALLOW
TERN
WARBLER
WREN

Give Me a Clue

Can you fill-in the blank tiles to create a word that solves each of the clues below?

Item purchased annually

	A			N			R

In-depth and rigorous

T			R				H

Relating to motion

	I					C

Pink-fleshed fish

	A			O	

Anagrams

Can you find the word that can be made from the following letters?

TGEDLEIDH

....

Can you find the two words that can be made from the following letters?

MECARHD

....

....

Can you find the three words that can be made from the following letters?

LWDASED

....

....

....

Themed Anagrams

Can you crack these anagrams relating to journalism?

MEAN STINGS

....

SLIM COUNT

....

BAD ACTORS

....

IDEAL TRIO

....

Word Wheel

Find as many words of 4+ letters as you can, using the letters in the wheel. All words must use the central letter. One word will use all the letters in the wheel.

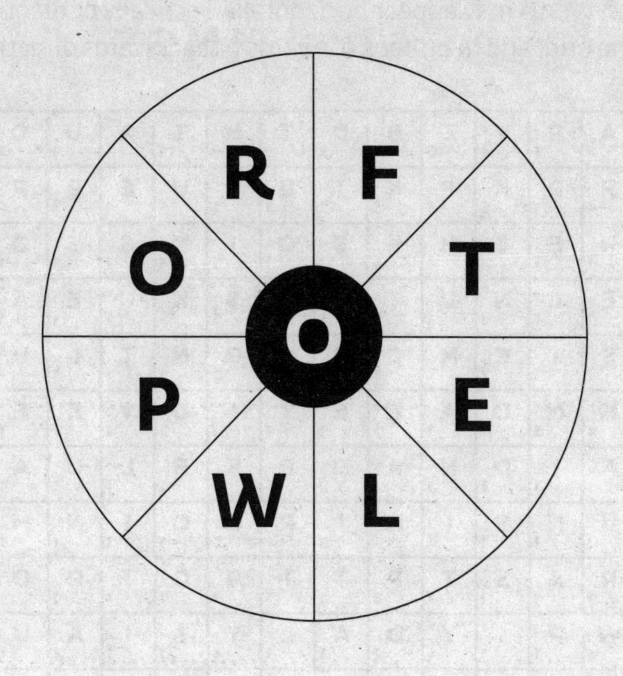

....

....

....

....

....

SCRABBLE™ Soup

Find the highest-scoring word you can in the grid of letters below by summing the values assigned to each letter tile in your word: for instance the word EXAMPLE would score 18 points. Words may appear horizontally, vertically or diagonally in the grid, and in either a forwards or backwards direction.

E 1	A 1	P 3	V 4	Z 10	B 3	D 2	T 1	M 3	T 1	A 1	U 1	C 3	S 1
P 3	F 4	R 1	K 5	P 3	K 5	I 1	B 3	C 3	U 1	E 1	B 3	F 4	U 1
M 3	R 1	E 1	E 1	H 4	K 5	S 1	O 1	I 1	M 3	S 1	E 1	O 1	I 1
E 1	E 1	L 1	N 1	U 1	T 1	C 3	O 1	B 3	K 5	U 1	E 1	A 1	S 1
M 3	S 1	I 1	C 3	M 3	C 3	R 1	S 1	Q 10	N 1	T 1	L 1	U 1	N 1
O 1	H 4	M 3	O 1	A 1	E 1	E 1	T 1	I 1	O 1	I 1	E 1	E 1	M 3
R 1	A 1	I 1	D 2	N 1	A 1	D 2	E 1	S 1	B 3	L 1	U 1	A 1	V 4
I 1	U 1	N 1	E 1	I 1	N 1	I 1	R 1	C 3	O 1	I 1	N 1	M 3	Y 4
A 1	R 1	A 1	S 1	T 1	P 3	T 1	I 1	R 1	D 2	T 1	R 1	O 1	M 3
L 1	W 4	R 1	I 1	Y 4	D 2	A 1	L 1	Y 4	I 1	I 1	A 1	U 1	A 1
Q 10	V 4	Y 4	G 2	A 1	I 1	B 3	M 3	I 1	E 1	E 1	V 4	R 1	U 1
Y 4	H 4	R 1	N 1	A 1	J 8	L 1	E 1	N 1	S 1	S 1	E 1	S 1	G 2
C 3	V 4	T 1	S 1	Z 10	T 1	E 1	I 1	G 2	O 1	F 4	L 1	E 1	W 4
E 1	L 1	E 1	V 4	E 1	R 1	E 1	T 1	B 3	E 1	L 1	I 1	E 1	F 4

Word Ladder

Use each of the tiles once to move from the word at the top of the ladder to the word at the bottom. You may only change one letter on each rung of the ladder, and must make a valid word on each rung. Use each of the Scrabble tiles once to do so.

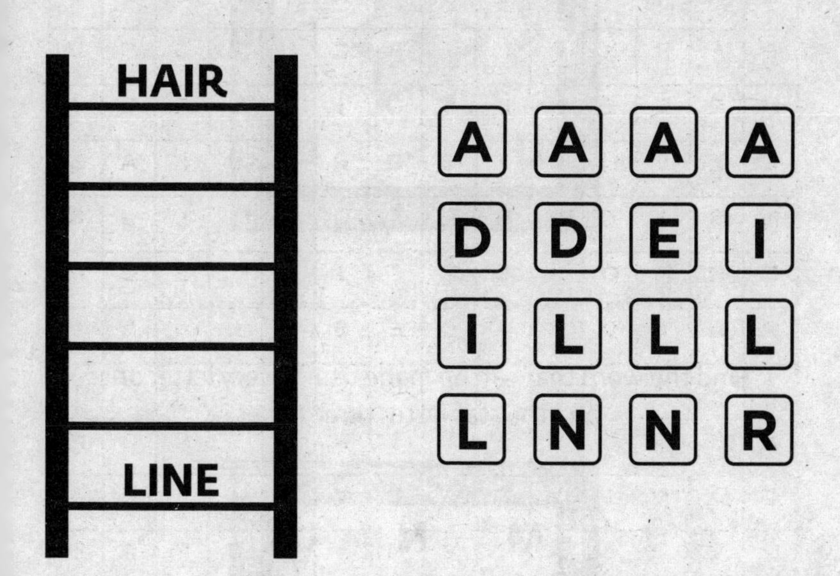

Star Letter

Find the word that can be made using every letter once, and the star letter twice.

....

Find the word that can be made using every letter once, and the star letter three times.

....

Consonant Crossword

Complete the crossword puzzle, in which all the vowels have already been placed. You must use each consonant tile listed once to fill the grid.

S T T T

Word Splits

Can you combine the word segments below to make three words?

AKN WE ESS

....

VI TY TI AC

....

IAN CE ALL

....

Link Words

Find the word that can replace the question marks on each line to make two new words or phrases. Use each of the Scrabble tiles once to do so.

UNDER ????? FALL

QUICK ???? SON

CHOPPING ????? GAME

A A B D
E E O P
R R S T
T W

Missing Vowels

All the vowels have been removed from three words. Use each of the vowel tiles below once to reconstruct the words.

1) QTY

2) SSW

3) GDNC

A A E E
E E I I
U U

Word Square

Use the Scrabble tiles provided to fill the grid, so that the answer to each crossword clue appears in the corresponding row of the grid. Once complete, the same answer words will also appear in the columns.

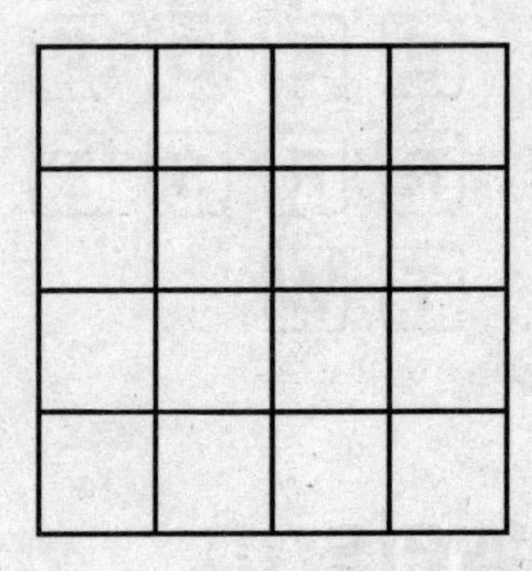

Female sheep (pl.)

Droop; lose energy

Otherwise

Pace

Unscramble

Can you unscramble the two types of flower
that have been mixed together below?

IRONIC ARTISAN

....

....

Can you unscramble the three items of stationery
that have been mixed together below?

LECTURE PLANS PERIL

....

....

....

Word Slider

Move each of the sliders up and down in order to form six-letter words in the middle row. Can you find five-or-more words?

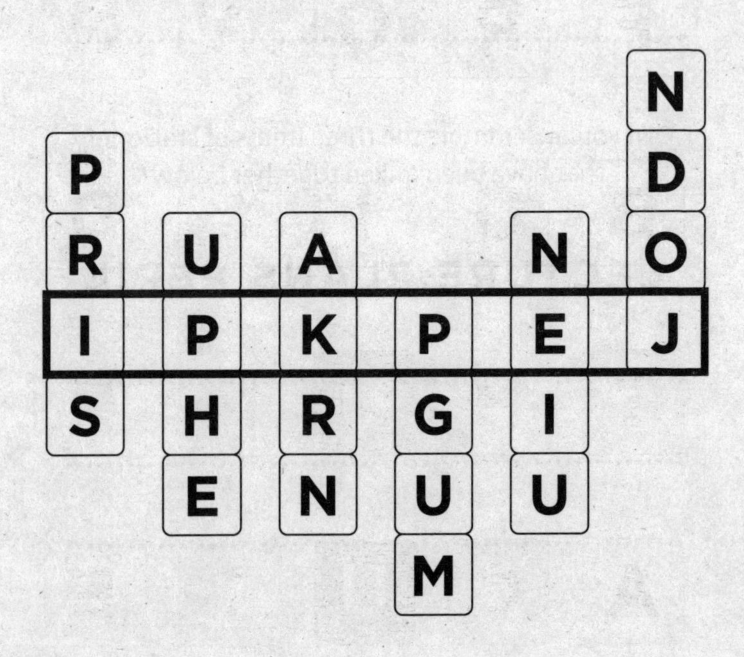

SCRABBLE™ Word

Can you guess the SCRABBLE™ Word? It is a word found in the Scrabble dictionary that does not repeat any letters. In each of the guesses below, a white background means the letter does not appear in the answer word. A black background means a letter is both found in the word and is in the correct position, whilst a grey background means a letter is found in the answer word, but in a different position.

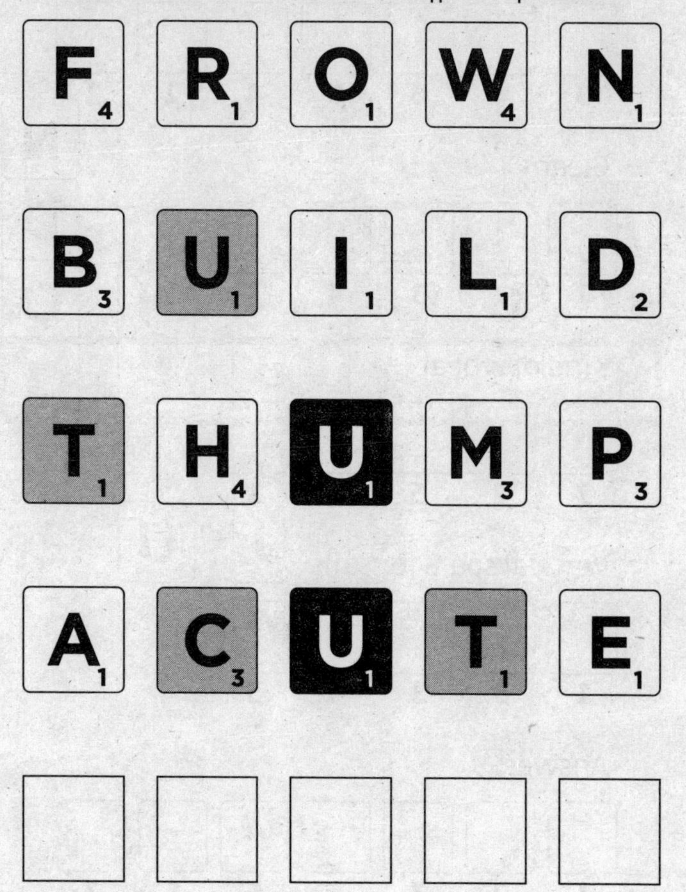

Value of solution tiles: 11 points

Seven Letters

A word composed of seven different letters has been created using Scrabble tiles. Can you answer the clues below to work out what that word is? Numbers indicate the position of each letter in the answer word.

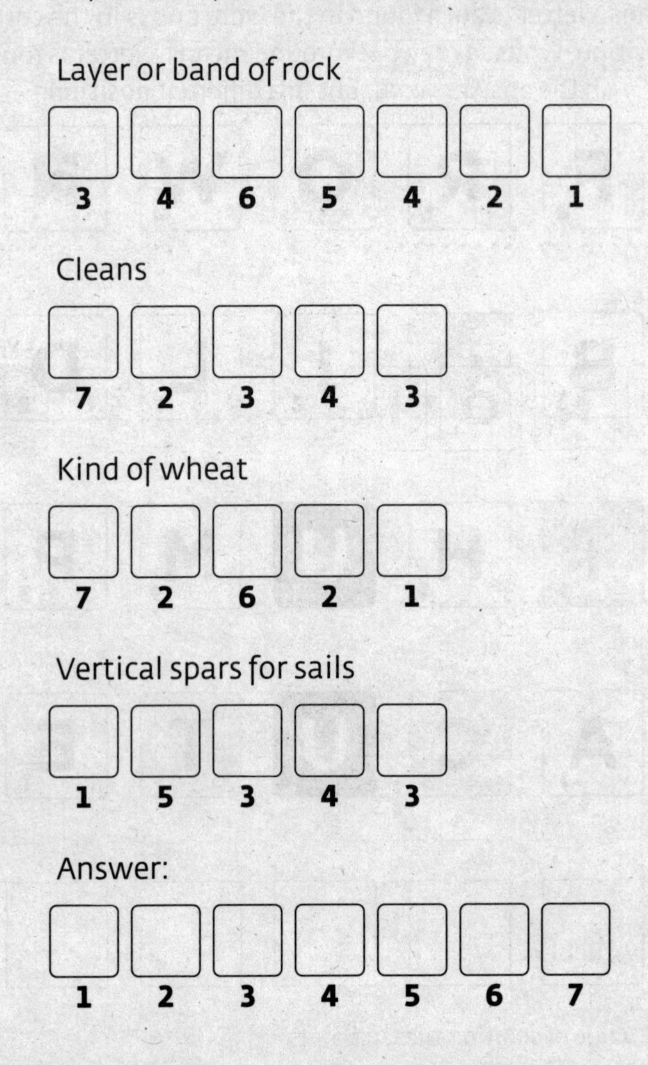

SCRABBLE™ Score

Make the highest score you can from each of the letter racks below. Add 50 points for a seven-letter word.

E 1	E 1	N 1	E 1	R 1	G 2	E 1	DOUBLE WORD SCORE

....

U 1	N 1	O 1	R 1	C 3	I 1	N 1	TRIPLE WORD SCORE

....

R 1	G 2	E 1	H 4	E 1	A 1	T 1	TRIPLE WORD SCORE

....

Wordsearch

Can you find all of these words relating to feelings and emotions from the Scrabble wordlist in the grid below? Words may appear horizontally, vertically or diagonally in either a forwards or backwards direction.

H	S	A	T	I	S	F	A	C	T	I	O	N	U
O	M	S	V	P	H	Z	G	M	P	T	Q	K	E
P	C	E	K	T	M	I	K	I	N	W	D	V	Y
E	O	R	Z	U	N	O	N	E	F	S	O	T	Q
S	U	E	F	Y	H	E	M	O	S	L	E	N	A
I	R	N	S	Y	T	T	M	E	I	M	R	T	N
R	A	I	H	A	N	I	N	E	P	T	H	A	G
P	G	T	H	E	D	M	L	A	S	G	A	Q	E
R	E	Y	T	O	L	N	T	I	I	U	B	L	R
U	S	N	J	A	Y	H	E	L	M	F	M	R	E
S	O	C	C	P	Y	U	E	S	B	U	M	A	J
C	H	O	V	P	S	D	Y	F	S	X	H	S	O
H	D	M	B	S	S	E	N	I	P	P	A	H	Y
E	X	C	I	T	E	M	E	N	T	L	A	F	B

AMUSEMENT	HAPPINESS
ANGER	HOPE
CALMNESS	HUMILITY
CONTENTMENT	JOY
COURAGE	LOVE
DELIGHT	SADNESS
ELATION	SATISFACTION
EMPATHY	SERENITY
EXCITEMENT	SURPRISE

Give Me a Clue

Can you fill-in the blank tiles to create a word that solves each of the clues below?

Fixed regular payment

S _ _ _ R _

Prolonged feud

_ E _ _ _ _ _ A

Succulent plant

_ A _ _ U _

Mysterious

E _ _ G _ _ _ I _

Anagrams

Can you find the word that can be made from the following letters?

OTXVERTER

....

Can you find the two words that can be made from the following letters?

CPLMOEI

....

....

Can you find the three words that can be made from the following letters?

TDHERA

....

....

....

Themed Anagrams

Can you crack these anagrams relating to space?

RUES VINE

....

RECAP FACTS

....

LATEST LIE

....

EDIT OARS

....

Word Wheel

Find as many words of 4+ letters as you can, using the letters in the wheel. All words must use the central letter. One word will use all the letters in the wheel.

SCRABBLE™ Soup

Find the highest-scoring word you can in the grid of letters below by summing the values assigned to each letter tile in your word: for instance the word EXAMPLE would score 18 points. Words may appear horizontally, vertically or diagonally in the grid, and in either a forwards or backwards direction.

G 2	I 1	R 1	A 1	O 1	G 2	A 1	R 1	I 1	S 1	H 4	K 5	P 3	H 4
A 1	E 1	D 2	I 1	S 1	T 1	I 1	N 1	C 3	T 1	V 4	E 1	R 1	P 3
G 2	H 4	O 1	U 1	L 1	I 1	S 1	H 4	W 4	F 4	T 1	E 1	O 1	T 1
P 3	E 1	N 1	I 1	T 1	E 1	N 1	C 3	E 1	O 1	A 1	R 1	N 1	P 3
T 1	B 3	L 1	U 1	R 1	B 3	S 1	T 1	T 1	R 1	Y 4	L 1	U 1	R 1
W 4	N 1	A 1	X 8	P 3	F 4	W 4	P 3	X 8	G 2	O 1	A 1	N 1	E 1
T 1	U 1	S 1	S 1	O 1	C 3	K 5	S 1	P 3	E 1	R 1	E 1	C 3	S 1
I 1	O 1	E 1	M 3	D 2	U 1	S 1	P 3	R 1	R 1	U 1	Q 10	I 1	E 1
B 3	I 1	L 1	L 1	B 3	O 1	A 1	R 1	D 2	L 1	E 1	T 1	A 1	I 1
U 1	U 1	V 4	A 1	I 1	A 1	U 1	P 3	E 1	C 3	F 4	P 3	T 1	R 1
P 3	E 1	R 1	T 1	A 1	I 1	N 1	S 1	P 3	S 1	U 1	A 1	I 1	E 1
I 1	T 1	U 1	B 3	R 1	A 1	I 1	L 1	L 1	E 1	L 1	O 1	O 1	Z 10
T 1	O 1	C 3	C 3	U 1	P 3	A 1	N 1	T 1	Z 10	T 1	P 3	N 1	O 1
H 4	Y 4	S 1	T 1	E 1	R 1	I 1	A 1	B 3	R 1	O 1	O 1	M 3	S 1

Word Ladder

Use each of the tiles once to move from the word at the top of the ladder to the word at the bottom. You may only change one letter on each rung of the ladder, and must make a valid word on each rung. Use each of the Scrabble tiles once to do so.

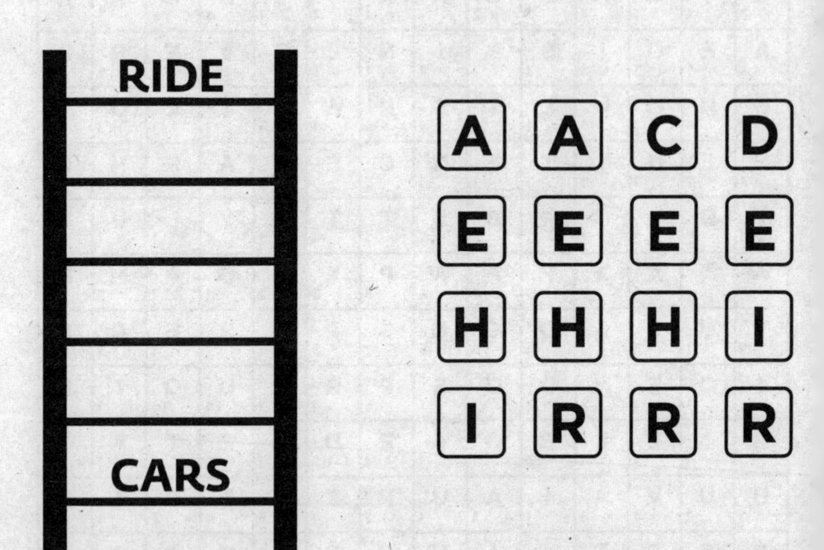

Star Letter

Find the word that can be made using every letter once, and the star letter twice.

....

Find the word that can be made using every letter once, and the star letter three times.

....

Consonant Crossword

Complete the crossword puzzle, in which all the vowels have already been placed. You must use each consonant tile listed once to fill the grid.

Word Splits

Can you combine the word segments below to make three words?

TI LA DE TU

....

ICS DEM ACA

....

OL AP IES OG

....

Link Words

Find the word that can replace the question marks on each line to make two new words or phrases. Use each of the Scrabble tiles once to do so.

MOUTH ????? MEAL

BOTTLE ???? ACCOUNT

FLAP ???? KNIFE

A A B C
C E E I
J K K N
P

Missing Vowels

All the vowels have been removed from three words. Use each of the vowel tiles below once to reconstruct the words.

1) MDW

2) LCV

3) ZLGY

A A E
E O O
O O O

Word Square

Use the Scrabble tiles provided to fill the grid, so that the answer to each crossword clue appears in the corresponding row of the grid. Once complete, the same answer words will also appear in the columns.

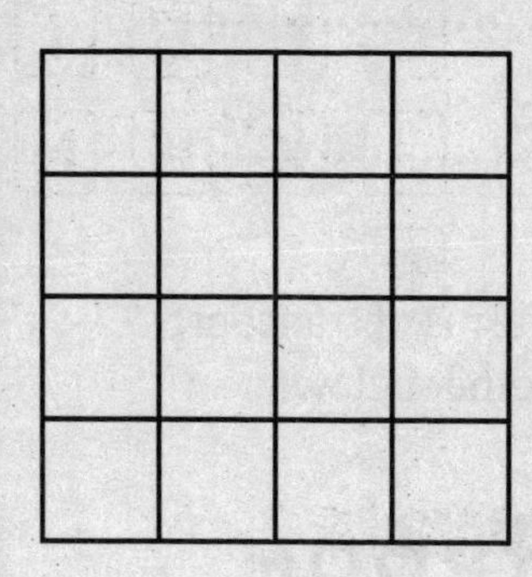

Song by two people

Reverse

In a tense state

Playthings

Unscramble

Can you unscramble the two sports that
have been mixed together below?

NOT KEY NICHES

....

....

Can you unscramble the three forms of transport
that have been mixed together below?

DEBTOR PLAYROOM

....

....

....

Word Slider

Move each of the sliders up and down in order to form six-letter words in the middle row. Can you find five-or-more words?

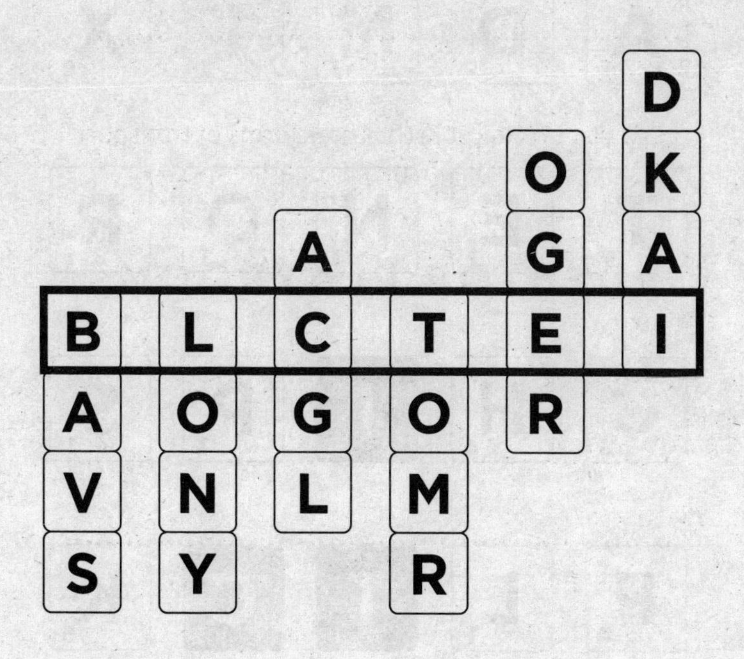

SCRABBLE™ Word

Can you guess the SCRABBLE™ Word? It is a word found in the Scrabble dictionary that does not repeat any letters. In each of the guesses below, a white background means the letter does not appear in the answer word. A black background means a letter is both found in the word and is in the correct position, whilst a grey background means a letter is found in the answer word, but in a different position.

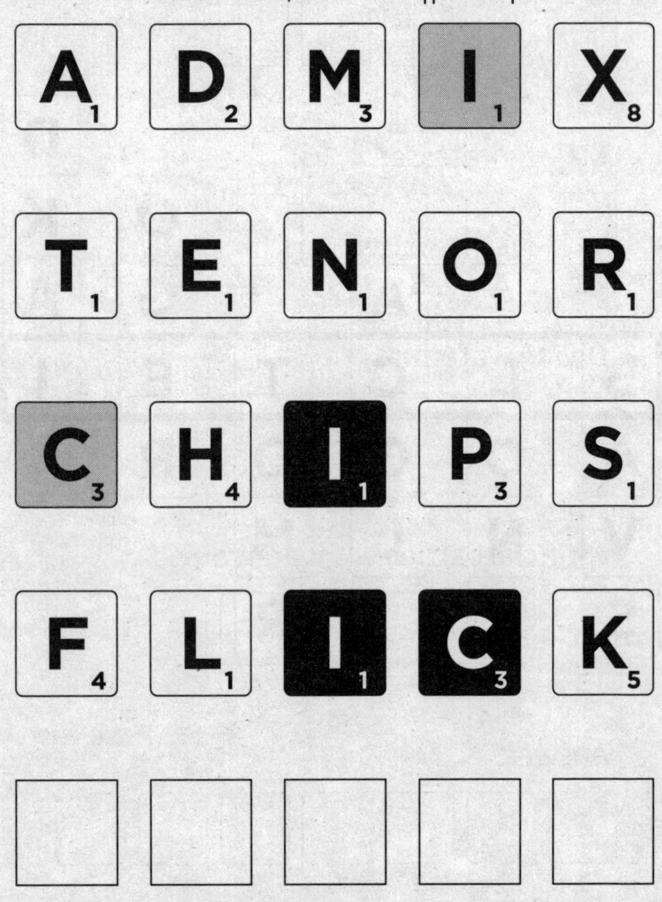

Value of solution tiles: 17 points

Seven Letters

A word composed of seven different letters has been created using Scrabble tiles. Can you answer the clues below to work out what that word is? Numbers indicate the position of each letter in the answer word.

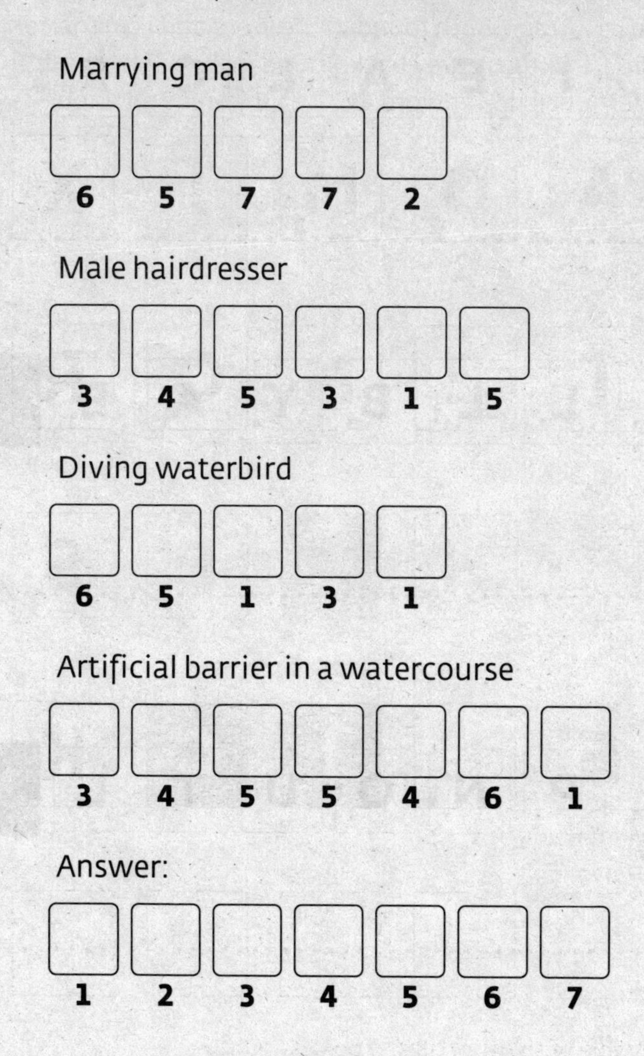

SCRABBLE™ Score

Make the highest score you can from each of the letter racks below. Add 50 points for a seven-letter word.

U 1 | I 1 | E 1 | A 1 | L 1 | C 3 | R 1

E 1 | L 1 | L 1 | B 3 | Y 4 | A 1 | E 1 | TRIPLE WORD SCORE

E 1 | P 3 | N 1 | O 1 | U 1 | T 1 | L 1 | DOUBLE SCORE ON 7TH LETTER

Wordsearch

Can you find all of these film-related words from the Scrabble wordlist in the grid below? Words may appear horizontally, vertically or diagonally in either a forwards or backwards direction.

D	Y	C	E	Y	D	E	M	O	C	Y	G	E	J
Y	O	Y	H	R	N	E	V	A	V	Y	N	R	L
R	H	C	O	A	S	W	D	Z	H	O	I	U	A
E	E	F	U	M	R	V	D	P	A	P	T	T	C
T	A	S	Z	M	E	A	A	Y	R	L	I	A	I
S	C	O	A	N	E	R	C	O	P	A	R	E	S
Y	L	R	T	E	G	N	D	T	M	M	W	F	U
M	S	U	I	O	L	U	T	B	E	A	T	O	M
Q	R	A	I	M	C	E	D	A	C	R	P	H	T
E	H	B	Z	T	E	C	R	H	R	D	I	O	N
T	A	N	I	M	A	T	I	O	N	Y	R	R	E
E	N	O	U	W	S	H	O	R	T	T	C	R	L
B	N	E	D	E	C	W	A	Y	A	O	S	O	I
S	H	I	S	T	O	R	I	C	A	L	B	R	S

ADVENTURE
ANIMATION
BIOGRAPHY
CHARACTER
COMEDY
CRIME
DOCUMENTARY
DRAMA
FEATURE
HISTORICAL
HORROR
MUSICAL
MYSTERY
PRODUCTION
RELEASE
SCRIPTWRITING
SHORT
SILENT

Give Me a Clue

Can you fill-in the blank tiles to create a word that solves each of the clues below?

Dish of marinated seafood

C _ V _ _ _ _

Film genre

_ H _ _ _ L _ R

Offspring

_ H _ _ _ R _ _

Having considerable worth

V _ _ U _ _ L _

Anagrams

Can you find the word that can be made from the following letters?

GNIOFMAL

....

Can you find the two words that can be made from the following letters?

GDEFNEI

....

....

Can you find the three words that can be made from the following letters?

TSREEDS

....

....

....

Themed Anagrams

Can you crack these anagrams relating to sewing?

PART NET

....

BINGO MESS

....

WONDER LEEK

....

BRIO REMEDY

....

Word Wheel

Find as many words of 4+ letters as you can, using the letters in the wheel. All words must use the central letter. One word will use all the letters in the wheel.

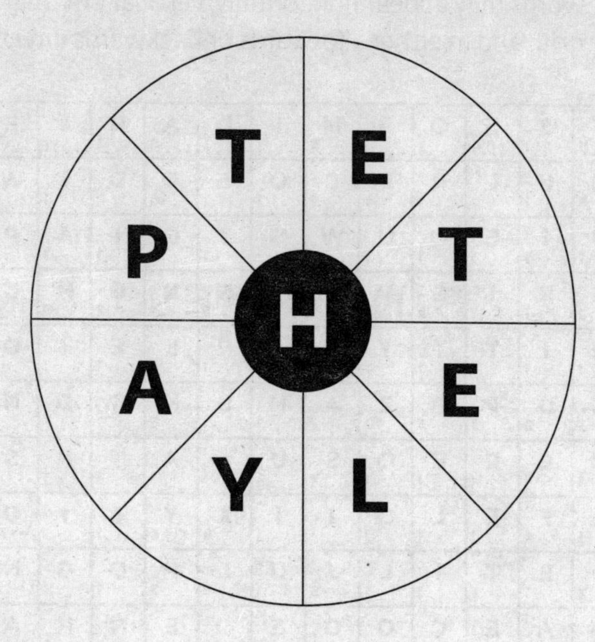

....

....

....

....

....

SCRABBLE™ Soup

Find the highest-scoring word you can in the grid of letters below by summing the values assigned to each letter tile in your word: for instance the word EXAMPLE would score 18 points. Words may appear horizontally, vertically or diagonally in the grid, and in either a forwards or backwards direction.

M 3	K 5	S 1	F 4	O 1	R 1	M 3	I 1	D 2	A 1	B 3	L 1	E 1	I 1
O 1	B 3	U 1	L 1	R 1	F 4	C 3	O 1	L 1	Q 10	D 2	I 1	W 4	M 3
E 1	U 1	I 1	E 1	O 1	U 1	W 4	S 1	T 1	Q 10	I 1	A 1	P 3	U 1
Q 10	A 1	R 1	I 1	G 2	V 4	T 1	I 1	N 1	N 1	G 2	M 3	C 3	M 3
G 2	R 1	I 1	T 1	T 1	Y 4	E 1	A 1	R 1	L 1	E 1	I 1	O 1	B 3
E 1	C 3	D 2	P 3	P 3	Z 10	A 1	N 1	S 1	K 5	S 1	D 2	N 1	L 1
F 4	O 1	E 1	R 1	E 1	O 1	S 1	U 1	L 1	A 1	T 1	N 1	S 1	E 1
F 4	L 1	F 4	E 1	L 1	O 1	T 1	I 1	X 8	Y 4	I 1	I 1	O 1	C 3
U 1	D 2	E 1	T 1	I 1	L 1	J 8	U 1	L 1	P 3	O 1	G 2	N 1	U 1
S 1	N 1	A 1	E 1	C 3	O 1	D 2	E 1	Q 10	E 1	N 1	H 4	A 1	Y 4
E 1	E 1	T 1	N 1	A 1	G 2	I 1	U 1	O 1	A 1	C 3	T 1	N 1	A 1
E 1	S 1	E 1	D 2	N 1	Y 4	E 1	Y 4	A 1	T 1	S 1	X 8	T 1	A 1
C 3	S 1	D 2	S 1	R 1	A 1	A 1	T 1	R 1	A 1	C 3	T 1	O 1	R 1
R 1	U 1	X 8	U 1	R 1	E 1	P 3	U 1	D 2	I 1	A 1	T 1	E 1	Q 10

Word Ladder

Use each of the tiles once to move from the word at the top of the ladder to the word at the bottom. You may only change one letter on each rung of the ladder, and must make a valid word on each rung. Use each of the Scrabble tiles once to do so.

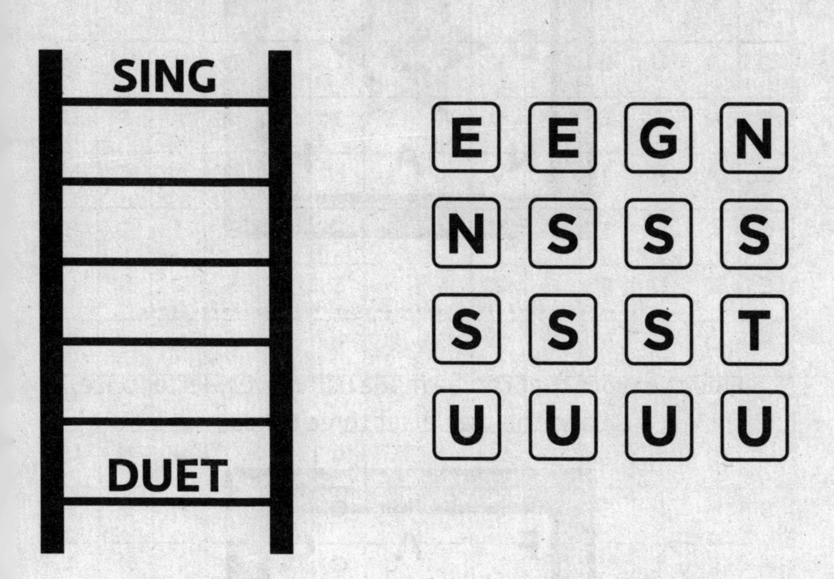

Star Letter

Find the word that can be made using every letter once, and the star letter twice.

Find the word that can be made using every letter once, and the star letter three times.

Consonant Crossword

Complete the crossword puzzle, in which all the vowels have already been placed. You must use each consonant tile listed once to fill the grid.

Word Splits

Can you combine the word segments below to make three words?

LLY ICA BAS

....

DY BO ARD GU

....

FLE ED CT DE

....

Link Words

Find the word that can replace the question marks on each line to make two new words or phrases. Use each of the Scrabble tiles once to do so.

SPRING ??????? FEED

KICK ????? STILL

GRAND ????? TUNER

A A C C
D E H I
I K N N
N O P S
T

Missing Vowels

All the vowels have been removed from three words. Use each of the vowel tiles below once to reconstruct the words.

1) RCV

2) CSCD

3) JWBN

A A A E
E E E E
I O

Word Square

Use the Scrabble tiles provided to fill the grid, so that the answer to each crossword clue appears in the corresponding row of the grid. Once complete, the same answer words will also appear in the columns.

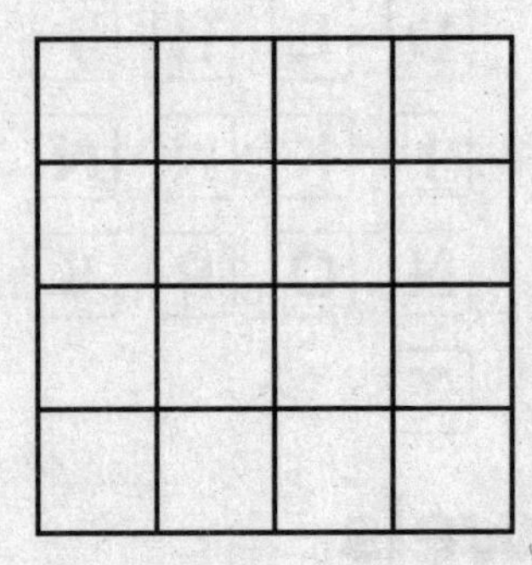

Thoroughfare

Unpleasant giant

Weapons

Office table

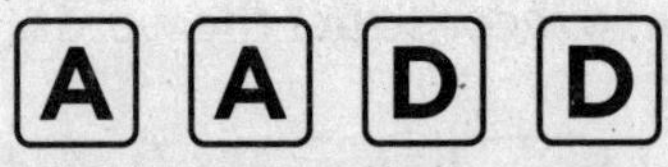

E E G K

M O O R

R R S S

Unscramble

Can you unscramble the two crafts that have been mixed together below?

TROTTING CHICKEN

....

....

Can you unscramble the three animals that have been mixed together below?

KEEP CUSHION SCHEME

....

....

....

Word Slider

Move each of the sliders up and down in order to form six-letter words in the middle row. Can you find five-or-more words?

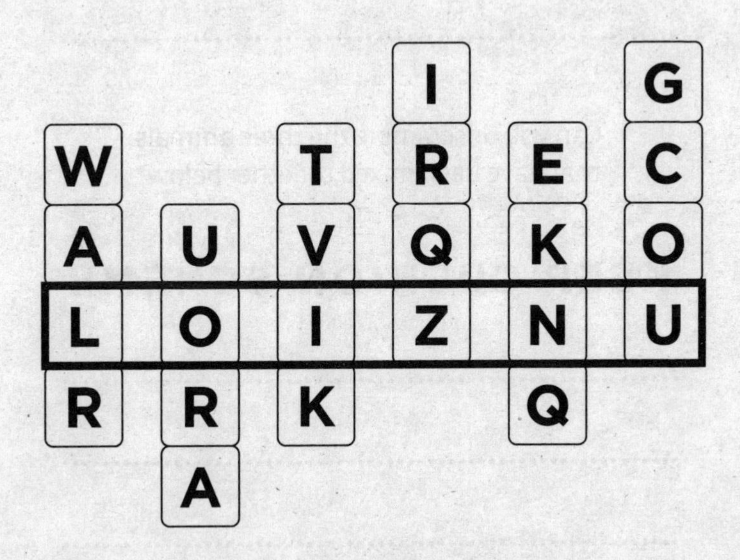

SCRABBLE™ Word

Can you guess the SCRABBLE™ Word? It is a word found in the Scrabble dictionary that does not repeat any letters. In each of the guesses below, a white background means the letter does not appear in the answer word. A black background means a letter is both found in the word and is in the correct position, whilst a grey background means a letter is found in the answer word, but in a different position.

Value of solution tiles: 7 points

Seven Letters

A word composed of seven different letters has been created using Scrabble tiles. Can you answer the clues below to work out what that word is? Numbers indicate the position of each letter in the answer word.

SCRABBLE™ Score

Make the highest score you can from each of the letter racks below. Add 50 points for a seven-letter word.

Z10 R1 N1 L1 P3 A1 A1

A1 D2 B3 O1 M3 L1 O1 TRIPLE WORD SCORE

Q10 X8 P3 O1 E1 T1 R1 TRIPLE WORD SCORE

Wordsearch

Can you find all of these car parts from the Scrabble wordlist in the grid below? Words may appear horizontally, vertically or diagonally in either a forwards or backwards direction.

K	Y	W	S	Q	E	Y	X	R	Q	T	R	S	O
G	T	Y	R	E	T	T	A	B	A	E	E	K	Q
E	L	X	A	R	D	B	U	T	H	A	M	H	C
S	M	T	E	W	O	R	S	S	T	S	Y	F	N
Z	J	I	K	N	B	O	A	N	E	V	S	O	Y
X	F	E	R	V	M	W	G	O	X	S	T	R	T
S	O	R	N	R	R	O	N	S	B	S	U	R	P
P	B	B	E	I	O	O	Y	W	I	H	A	F	Q
E	W	H	R	G	G	R	T	P	S	D	S	U	I
A	T	E	H	A	R	N	G	A	I	U	Y	A	Y
K	G	F	K	X	E	A	E	O	I	Q	P	T	D
E	I	U	M	E	V	G	H	B	R	D	F	B	O
R	F	O	O	R	N	U	S	C	N	N	A	M	C
T	P	I	T	S	E	R	D	A	E	H	N	R	L

AXLE
BATTERY
CHARGER
DASHBOARD
ENGINE
FAN
FUSE
GEARBOX
HEADREST
MIRROR
PISTON
RADIATOR
RADIO
SEAT
SPEAKER
SUNROOF
THERMOSTAT
WASHER

Give Me a Clue

Can you fill-in the blank tiles to create a word that solves each of the clues below?

Vegetable

	S				A		U	

Area of land between hills

V				E	

Trailblazer

	I		N			

Chewy sweet

C				M		

Anagrams

Can you find the word that can be made from the following letters?

YSARSGOL

....

Can you find the two words that can be made from the following letters?

ISDINHEF

....

....

Can you find the three words that can be made from the following letters?

EATIDL

....

....

....

Themed Anagrams

Can you crack these anagrams relating to gymnastics?

AQUA BEERS

....

WATCH REEL

....

SONGBIRD RAP

....

ALMOST SURE

....

Word Wheel

Find as many words of 4+ letters as you can, using the letters in the wheel. All words must use the central letter. One word will use all the letters in the wheel.

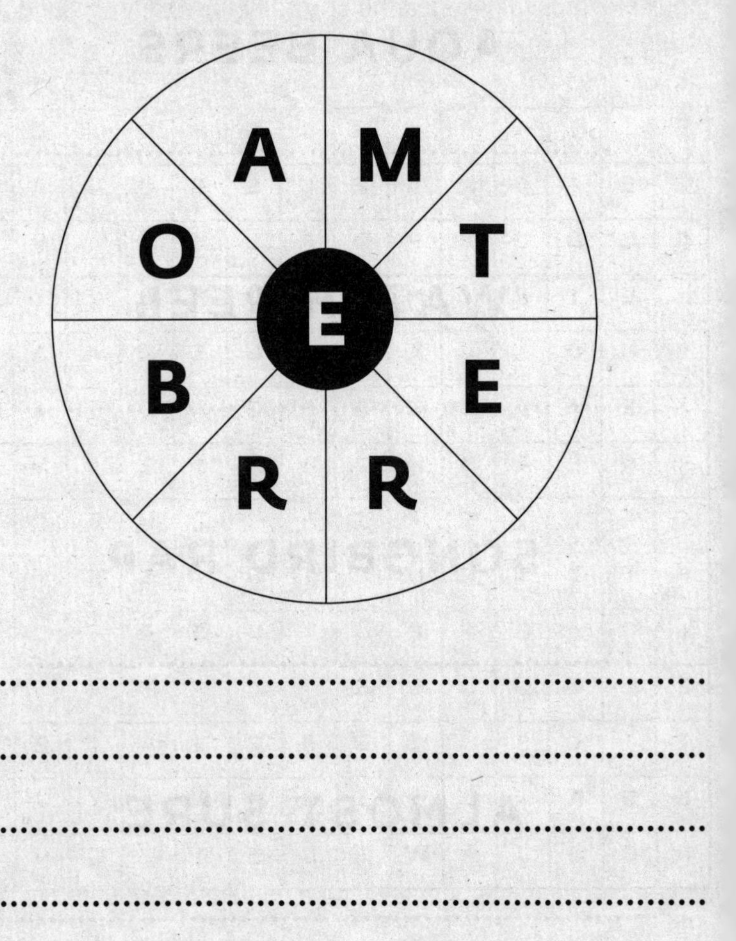

SCRABBLE™ Soup

Find the highest-scoring word you can in the grid of letters below by summing the values assigned to each letter tile in your word: for instance the word EXAMPLE would score 18 points. Words may appear horizontally, vertically or diagonally in the grid, and in either a forwards or backwards direction.

H 4	T 1	I 1	A 1	P 3	L 1	R 1	X 8	G 2	B 3	O 1	X 8	C 3	P 3
E 1	E 1	A 1	D 2	R 1	L 1	E 1	C 3	S 1	E 1	O 1	P 3	A 1	D 2
E 1	G 2	D 2	G 2	E 1	P 3	D 2	A 1	L 1	X 8	C 3	I 1	P 3	E 1
I 1	E 1	I 1	E 1	Y 4	M 3	U 1	U 1	U 1	H 4	O 1	T 1	T 1	R 1
E 1	N 1	D 2	L 1	E 1	A 1	C 3	S 1	G 2	I 1	N 1	A 1	A 1	A 1
A 1	E 1	A 1	A 1	D 2	C 3	A 1	E 1	G 2	B 3	D 2	T 1	I 1	D 2
T 1	R 1	E 1	T 1	M 3	H 4	T 1	W 4	A 1	I 1	E 1	T 1	N 1	I 1
C 3	A 1	V 4	I 1	E 1	I 1	I 1	A 1	R 1	T 1	N 1	E 1	C 3	C 3
H 4	T 1	T 1	N 1	F 4	N 1	N 1	Y 4	D 2	I 1	S 1	R 1	Y 4	A 1
A 1	O 1	A 1	O 1	F 4	E 1	G 2	K 5	U 1	O 1	E 1	S 1	U 1	T 1
P 3	R 1	O 1	U 1	U 1	S 1	S 1	F 4	K 5	N 1	T 1	W 4	S 1	E 1
T 1	I 1	L 1	S 1	H 4	I 1	B 3	E 1	R 1	N 1	A 1	T 1	E 1	P 3
E 1	S 1	A 1	N 1	D 2	W 4	I 1	C 3	H 4	E 1	S 1	Y 4	J 8	A 1
R 1	C 3	G 2	J 8	A 1	W 4	T 1	E 1	G 2	A 1	V 4	O 1	U 1	C 3

Word Ladder

Use each of the tiles once to move from the word at the top of the ladder to the word at the bottom. You may only change one letter on each rung of the ladder, and must make a valid word on each rung. Use each of the Scrabble tiles once to do so.

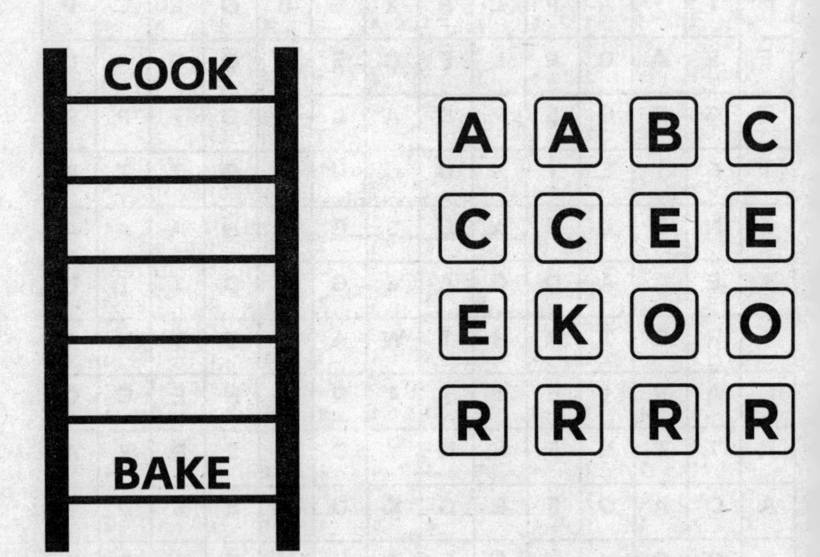

Star Letter

Find the word that can be made using every letter once, and the star letter twice.

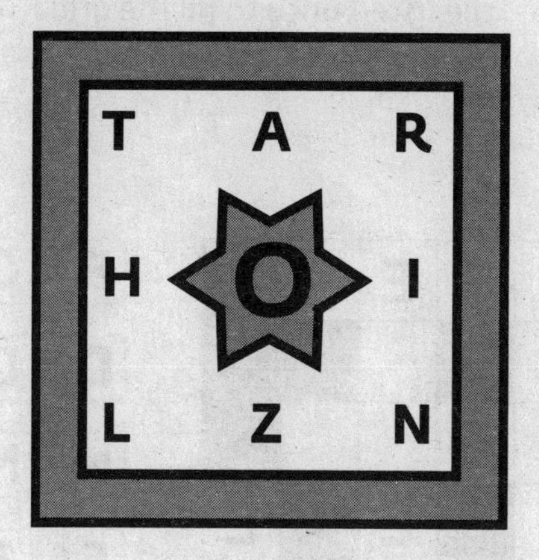

....

Find the word that can be made using every letter once, and the star letter three times.

....

Consonant Crossword

Complete the crossword puzzle, in which all the vowels have already been placed. You must use each consonant tile listed once to fill the grid.

Word Splits

Can you combine the word segments
below to make three words?

LAT EMU ION

....

AI NS UNT FO

....

LE ACA GU MO

....

Link Words

Find the word that can replace the question marks on each line to make two new words or phrases. Use each of the Scrabble tiles once to do so.

FORGOT ??? FOLD

MINE ????? WORK

SLEDGE ?????? HEAD

A D E E
E F H I
L M M N
R T

Missing Vowels

All the vowels have been removed from three words. Use each of the vowel tiles below once to reconstruct the words.

1) CCLRT

2) PRFM

3) VNSN

A A E E
E E E E
I O U

Word Square

Use the Scrabble tiles provided to fill the grid, so that the answer to each crossword clue appears in the corresponding row of the grid. Once complete, the same answer words will also appear in the columns.

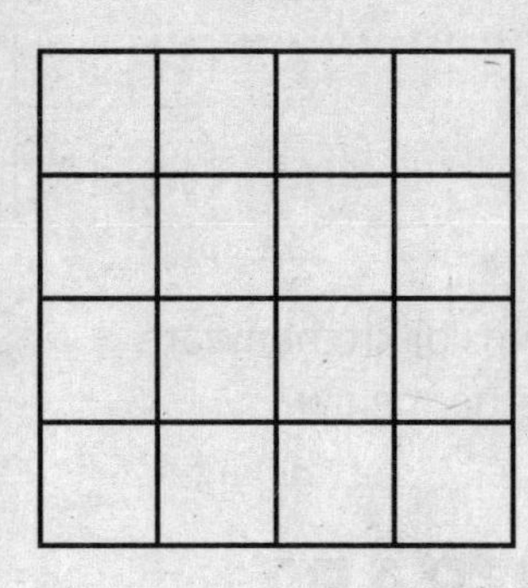

Great show or display

Quartzlike gem

Mother

Scheme

P P P P

Unscramble

Can you unscramble the two items of clothing that have been mixed together below?

JUST RETRO CAKES

....

....

Can you unscramble the three items of kitchenware that have been mixed together below?

REGRET MAIN PART

....

....

....

Word Slider

Move each of the sliders up and down in order to form six-letter words in the middle row. Can you find five-or-more words?

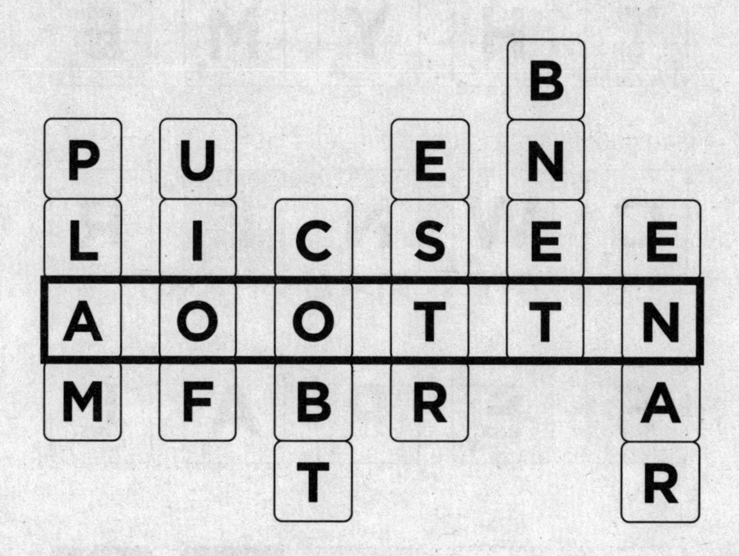

SCRABBLE™ Word

Can you guess the SCRABBLE™ Word? It is a word found in the Scrabble dictionary that does not repeat any letters. In each of the guesses below, a white background means the letter does not appear in the answer word. A black background means a letter is both found in the word and is in the correct position, whilst a grey background means a letter is found in the answer word, but in a different position.

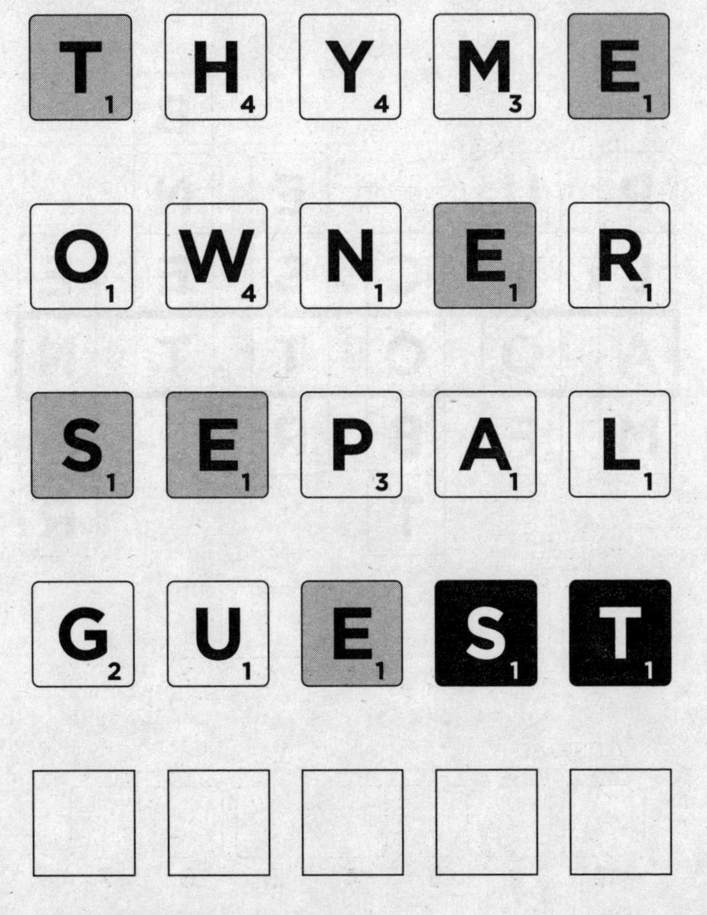

Value of solution tiles: 12 points

Seven Letters

A word composed of seven different letters has been created using Scrabble tiles. Can you answer the clues below to work out what that word is? Numbers indicate the position of each letter in the answer word.

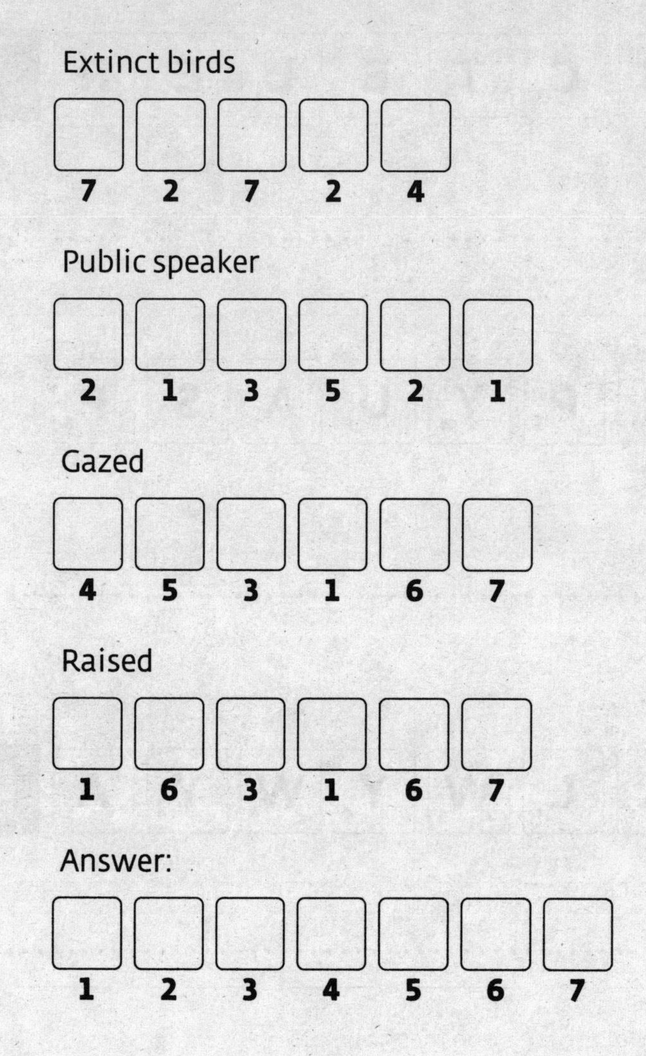

SCRABBLE™ Score

Make the highest score you can from each of the letter racks below. Add 50 points for a seven-letter word.

N 1 | C 3 | T 1 | E 1 | L 1 | E 1 | R 1 | DOUBLE SCORE ON 1ST LETTER

....

R 1 | P 3 | Y 4 | U 1 | A 1 | S 1 | P 3

....

A 1 | L 1 | W 4 | Y 4 | W 4 | Y 4 | A 1 | DOUBLE WORD SCORE

....

Wordsearch

Can you find all of these salad components from the Scrabble wordlist in the grid below? Words may appear horizontally, vertically or diagonally in either a forwards or backwards direction.

```
I P X O T O R R A C A A W D
I X M T D L Q Q A H G G Z R
E O W A I C G O K A H G K A
Q E D T U J H O R G S E R D
J L D O O M N E U K I C H I
E G I P C I P G E Q F U C S
R B L U O P F T S S K T E H
P E L N E Z N I W U E T L B
O G C P C F D A Y L E E E G
R R G U A C L B Q E U L R A
K S G K R N B E V M I I Y R
D G H A U M N E C O D D Y L
S E B T N S X F Z N V Z Q I
J G C D G O T A M O T O G C
```

BEEF	**LEMON**
CARROT	**LETTUCE**
CELERY	**ONION**
CHEESE	**PEPPER**
CRAB	**PORK**
DILL	**POTATO**
EGG	**RADISH**
FISH	**TOMATO**
GARLIC	**WALNUT**

Give Me a Clue

Can you fill-in the blank tiles to create a word that solves each of the clues below?

Remedy for an illness

_ E _ _ C _ _ E

Large amount of money

F _ _ _ _ N _

Very spacious

C _ _ E _ N _ _ _

Long journey at sea

_ O _ _ G _

Anagrams

Can you find the word that can be made from the following letters?

LUNIAJBT

....

Can you find the two words that can be made from the following letters?

THGPNOAE

....

....

Can you find the three words that can be made from the following letters?

SEDTUR

....

....

....

Themed Anagrams

Can you crack these anagrams relating to pottery?

NEARER WHEAT

....

PEARL COIN

....

RIGHT NOW

....

CAR MICE

....

Word Wheel

Find as many words of 4+ letters as you can, using the letters in the wheel. All words must use the central letter. One word will use all the letters in the wheel.

....

....

....

....

....

SCRABBLE™ Soup

Find the highest-scoring word you can in the grid of letters below by summing the values assigned to each letter tile in your word: for instance the word EXAMPLE would score 18 points. Words may appear horizontally, vertically or diagonally in the grid, and in either a forwards or backwards direction.

B 3	L 1	E 1	J 8	E 1	S 1	I 1	D 2	E 1	S 1	K 5	T 1	O 1	P 3
U 1	J 8	T 1	A 1	U 1	A 1	P 3	I 1	E 1	U 1	E 1	U 1	W 4	R 1
R 1	G 2	U 1	A 1	N 1	F 4	K 5	A 1	R 1	X 8	I 1	I 1	V 4	S 1
S 1	R 1	U 1	B 3	I 1	E 1	E 1	R 1	E 1	N 1	D 2	E 1	U 1	T 1
A 1	A 1	T 1	S 1	F 4	S 1	L 1	O 1	D 2	I 1	T 1	O 1	V 4	D 2
R 1	N 1	I 1	O 1	I 1	T 1	O 1	O 1	M 3	E 1	E 1	U 1	Q 10	I 1
I 1	D 2	A 1	L 1	E 1	T 1	O 1	N 1	S 1	U 1	D 2	T 1	V 4	S 1
N 1	M 3	N 1	U 1	S 1	R 1	E 1	Y 4	T 1	X 8	E 1	R 1	P 3	C 3
G 2	O 1	G 2	T 1	I 1	S 1	H 4	J 8	P 3	R 1	G 2	U 1	O 1	U 1
U 1	T 1	E 1	I 1	S 1	F 4	L 1	B 3	I 1	R 1	R 1	N 1	L 1	S 1
I 1	H 4	L 1	O 1	R 1	G 2	A 1	T 1	Z 10	U 1	E 1	J 8	L 1	S 1
L 1	E 1	I 1	N 1	U 1	X 8	T 1	F 4	L 1	A 1	E 1	E 1	E 1	E 1
T 1	R 1	C 3	R 1	S 1	H 4	A 1	Y 4	Y 4	I 1	S 1	D 2	N 1	Y 4
Y 4	P 3	A 1	C 3	O 1	N 1	S 1	I 1	S 1	T 1	E 1	N 1	T 1	F 4

Word Ladder

Use each of the tiles once to move from the word at the top of the ladder to the word at the bottom. You may only change one letter on each rung of the ladder, and must make a valid word on each rung. Use each of the Scrabble tiles once to do so.

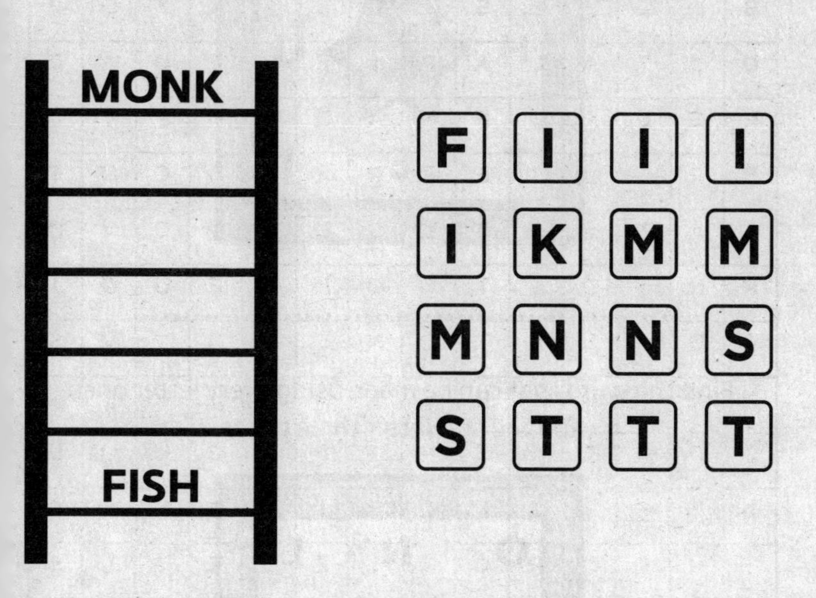

Star Letter

Find the word that can be made using every letter once, and the star letter twice.

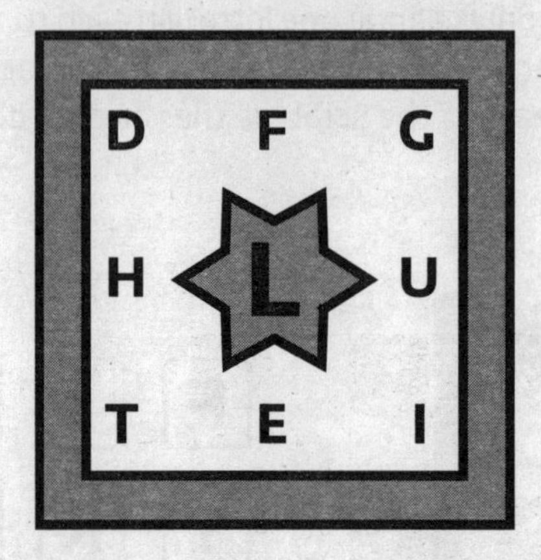

....

Find the word that can be made using every letter once, and the star letter three times.

....

Consonant Crossword

Complete the crossword puzzle, in which all the vowels have already been placed. You must use each consonant tile listed once to fill the grid.

Word Splits

Can you combine the word segments
below to make three words?

RE ED SS IMP

....

ENT ION INT

....

RY NDA GE LE

....

Link Words

Find the word that can replace the question marks on each line to make two new words or phrases. Use each of the Scrabble tiles once to do so.

LETTER ???? LINE

LONG ???? SUIT

TOOTH ???? POCKET

A C D E

H I J K

M P P U

Missing Vowels

All the vowels have been removed from three words. Use each of the vowel tiles below once to reconstruct the words.

1) GRRSN

2) RBG

3) PNSV

A

E

I

Word Square

Use the Scrabble tiles provided to fill the grid, so that the answer to each crossword clue appears in the corresponding row of the grid. Once complete, the same answer words will also appear in the columns.

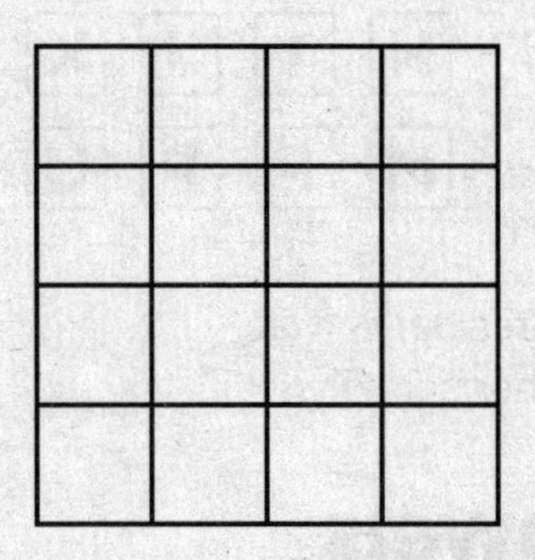

Containers

Fever or shivering fit

Corrode

Hardens

G J R R

S S S S

T T U U

Unscramble

Can you unscramble the two words relating to bad weather that have been mixed together below?

HAUNTED RICHER URN

....

....

Can you unscramble the three herbs that have been mixed together below?

LUCID SNAIL LIMB

....

....

....

Word Slider

Move each of the sliders up and down in order to form six-letter words in the middle row. Can you find five-or-more words?

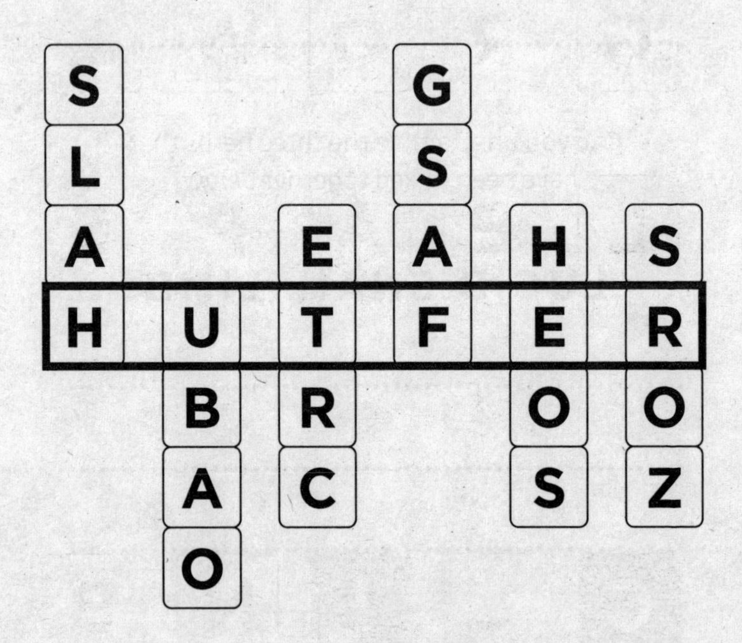

SCRABBLE™ Word

Can you guess the SCRABBLE™ Word? It is a word found in the Scrabble dictionary that does not repeat any letters. In each of the guesses below, a white background means the letter does not appear in the answer word. A black background means a letter is both found in the word and is in the correct position, whilst a grey background means a letter is found in the answer word, but in a different position.

Value of solution tiles: 11 points

Seven Letters

A word composed of seven different letters has been created using Scrabble tiles. Can you answer the clues below to work out what that word is? Numbers indicate the position of each letter in the answer word.

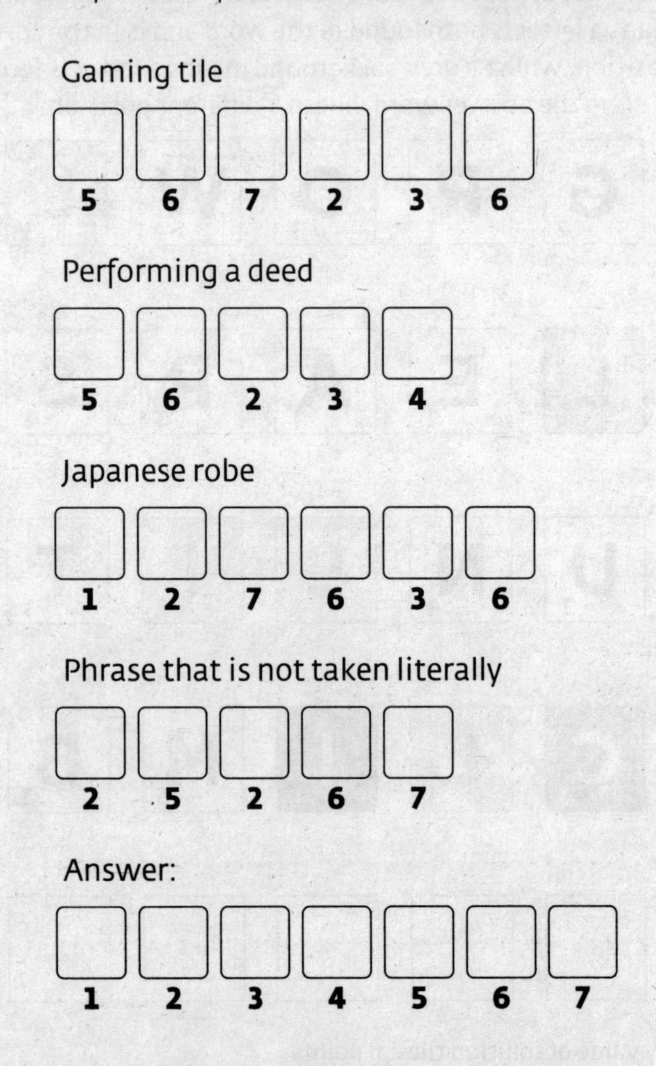

SCRABBLE™ Score

Make the highest score you can from each of the letter racks below. Add 50 points for a seven-letter word.

I 1	E 1	M 3	B 3	Z 10	O 1	V 4	DOUBLE WORD SCORE

L 1	I 1	Q 10	C 3	C 3	U 1	T 1	TRIPLE SCORE ON 1ST LETTER

U 1	O 1	E 1	I 1	L 1	M 3	I 1	DOUBLE WORD SCORE

Wordsearch

Can you find all of these words containing 'X' from the Scrabble wordlist in the grid below? Words may appear horizontally, vertically or diagonally in either a forwards or backwards direction.

O	E	Z	E	N	O	H	P	O	X	A	S	R	U
M	S	I	L	A	I	T	N	E	T	S	I	X	E
M	E	G	A	P	I	X	E	L	F	R	Q	Y	G
Q	C	Z	C	D	E	T	C	E	P	X	E	N	U
X	O	D	O	H	T	R	O	N	U	X	Y	P	E
G	M	E	E	O	D	W	H	B	P	R	R	X	X
K	P	X	X	X	W	W	E	E	A	E	P	F	T
O	L	A	I	C	D	E	N	I	Y	R	L	O	I
O	E	L	S	T	S	D	L	A	E	E	Q	X	N
B	X	E	T	W	I	I	P	S	X	G	D	H	C
T	I	R	A	T	X	X	S	I	X	G	B	O	T
X	T	X	U	U	A	I	B	J	D	P	B	L	I
E	Y	R	A	T	O	L	Q	E	K	V	R	E	O
T	E	W	O	N	E	X	T	E	R	N	A	L	N

AUXILIARY	FLEXIBLE
BEESWAX	FOXHOLE
COEXIST	MEGAPIXEL
COMPLEXITY	RELAXED
EXISTENTIALISM	SAXOPHONE
EXPENDITURE	TAXPAYER
EXPRESSION	TEXTBOOK
EXTERNAL	UNEXPECTED
EXTINCTION	UNORTHODOX

Give Me a Clue

Can you fill-in the blank tiles to create a word
that solves each of the clues below?

Network of rabbit burrows

_	A	_	R	_	_

Sedimentary rock

_	I	_	_	S	_	_	_	E

Unvarying

U	_	_	F	_	_	_

Form of carbon

C	_	_	_	C	_	_	L

Anagrams

Can you find the word that can be made from the following letters?

UIGOLNETD

....

Can you find the two words that can be made from the following letters?

DIORUTNCE

....

....

Can you find the three words that can be made from the following letters?

LESKE

....

....

....

Themed Anagrams

Can you crack these anagrams of chemical elements?

MILL BUYER

....

IRON FUEL

....

UNLIT MAP

....

STORM UNIT

....

Word Wheel

Find as many words of 4+ letters as you can, using the letters in the wheel. All words must use the central letter. One word will use all the letters in the wheel.

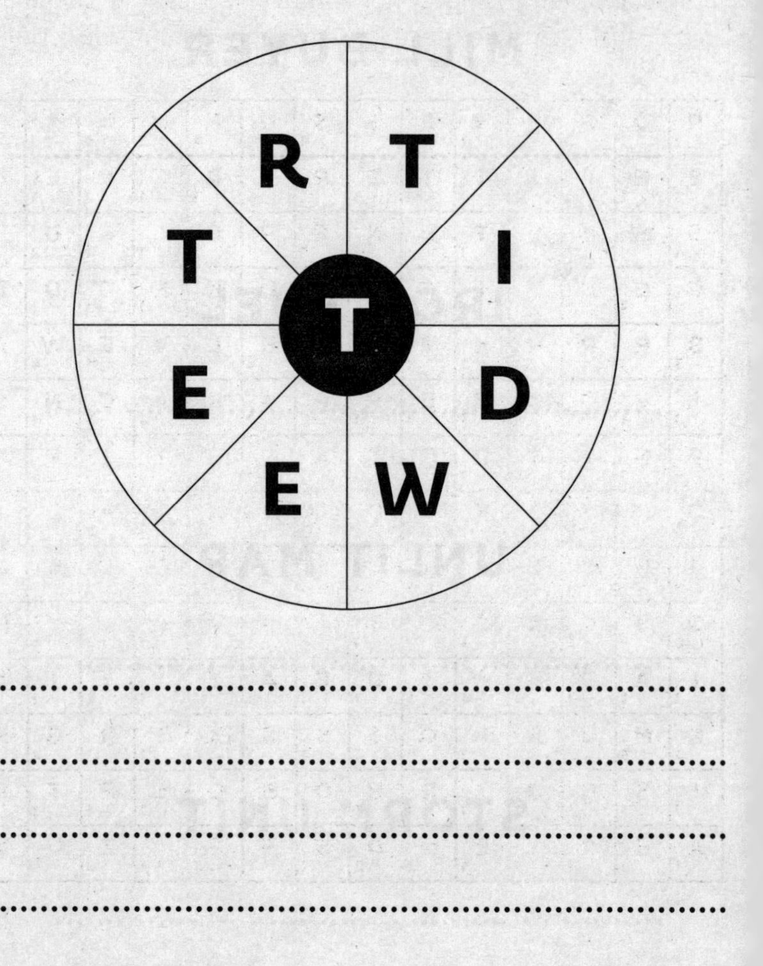

SCRABBLE™ Soup

Find the highest-scoring word you can in the grid of letters below by summing the values assigned to each letter tile in your word: for instance the word EXAMPLE would score 18 points. Words may appear horizontally, vertically or diagonally in the grid, and in either a forwards or backwards direction.

R 1	O 1	P 3	P 3	R 1	E 1	S 1	S 1	U 1	F 4	M 3	Y 4	I 1	H 4
B 3	E 1	J 8	I 1	T 1	T 1	E 1	R 1	P 3	R 1	E 1	E 1	E 1	U 1
S 1	W 4	E 1	E 1	T 1	E 1	N 1	E 1	R 1	C 3	L 1	S 1	D 2	V 4
G 2	C 3	U 1	T 1	I 1	C 3	L 1	E 1	D 2	K 5	E 1	P 3	O 1	B 3
B 3	R 1	R 1	R 1	K 5	T 1	O 1	U 1	H 4	L 1	V 4	E 1	W 4	A 1
I 1	V 4	O 1	X 8	B 3	E 1	R 1	P 3	I 1	K 5	A 1	C 3	N 1	S 1
F 4	N 1	I 1	C 3	R 1	O 1	T 1	A 1	T 1	E 1	T 1	I 1	P 3	T 1
O 1	M 3	J 8	S 1	E 1	A 1	D 2	L 1	E 1	X 8	I 1	A 1	L 1	I 1
J 8	R 1	C 3	E 1	C 3	R 1	F 4	I 1	P 3	E 1	O 1	L 1	A 1	O 1
Q 10	E 1	C 3	R 1	C 3	O 1	I 1	I 1	S 1	R 1	N 1	L 1	Y 4	N 1
I 1	A 1	R 1	H 4	W 4	T 1	U 1	E 1	A 1	Y 4	I 1	Y 4	I 1	L 1
K 5	M 3	U 1	A 1	A 1	O 1	I 1	S 1	S 1	X 8	T 1	R 1	G 2	R 1
I 1	S 1	C 3	Q 10	T 1	R 1	B 3	O 1	B 3	O 1	S 1	R 1	T 1	E 1
A 1	E 1	R 1	R 1	E 1	O 1	D 2	S 1	N 1	P 3	I 1	Z 10	U 1	Y 4

Word Ladder

Use each of the tiles once to move from the word at the top of the ladder to the word at the bottom. You may only change one letter on each rung of the ladder, and must make a valid word on each rung. Use each of the Scrabble tiles once to do so.

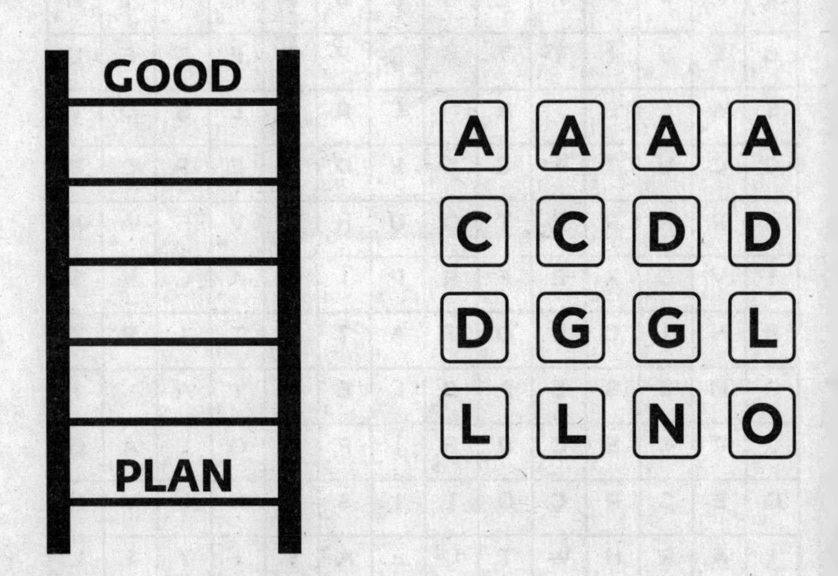

Star Letter

Find the word that can be made using every letter once, and the star letter twice.

....

Find the word that can be made using every letter once, and the star letter three times.

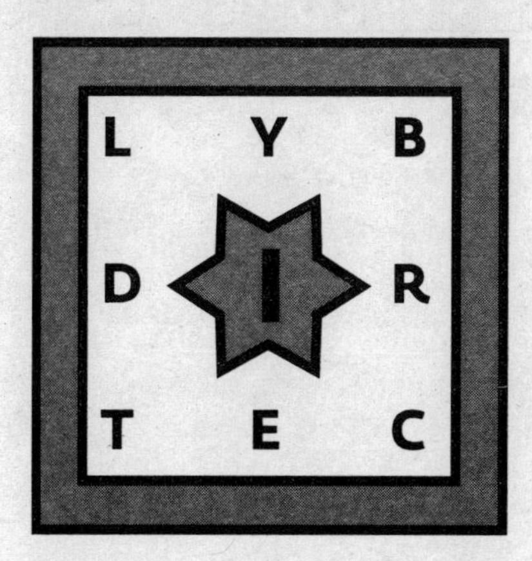

....

Consonant Crossword

Complete the crossword puzzle, in which all the vowels have already been placed. You must use each consonant tile listed once to fill the grid.

Word Splits

Can you combine the word segments below to make three words?

OD WO KER PEC

....

NSA SE ON TI

....

LLY TH FU TRU

....

Link Words

Find the word that can replace the question marks on each line to make two new words or phrases. Use each of the Scrabble tiles once to do so.

PAPER ???? GROUND

MATCH ??? WOOD

CROSS ???? BRUSH

A A B B

C H I K

O R X

Missing Vowels

All the vowels have been removed from three words. Use each of the vowel tiles below once to reconstruct the words.

1) TSNM

2) CLYT

3) PBT

A A A

E E I

O U U

Word Square

Use the Scrabble tiles provided to fill the grid, so that the answer to each crossword clue appears in the corresponding row of the grid. Once complete, the same answer words will also appear in the columns.

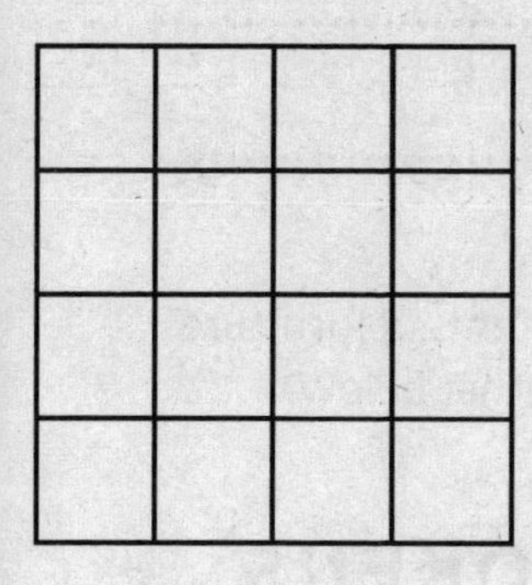

Flying mammals

Surrounding glow

Confine; snare

Drains of energy

A A A A

A B P P

R R S S

S T T U

Unscramble

Can you unscramble the two types of wood that have been mixed together below?

MANAGE HOLY MAP

....

....

Can you unscramble the three items of furniture that have been mixed together below?

SOLD TOFU TOKENS

....

....

....

Word Slider

Move each of the sliders up and down in order to form six-letter words in the middle row. Can you find five-or-more words?

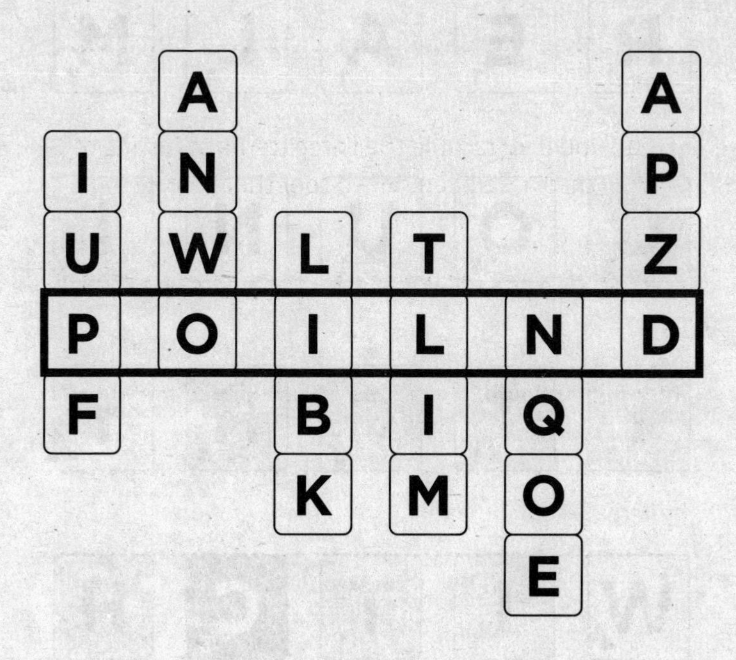

SCRABBLE™ Word

Can you guess the SCRABBLE™ Word? It is a word found in the Scrabble dictionary that does not repeat any letters. In each of the guesses below, a white background means the letter does not appear in the answer word. A black background means a letter is both found in the word and is in the correct position, whilst a grey background means a letter is found in the answer word, but in a different position.

Value of solution tiles: 14 points

Seven Letters

A word composed of seven different letters has been created using Scrabble tiles. Can you answer the clues below to work out what that word is? Numbers indicate the position of each letter in the answer word.

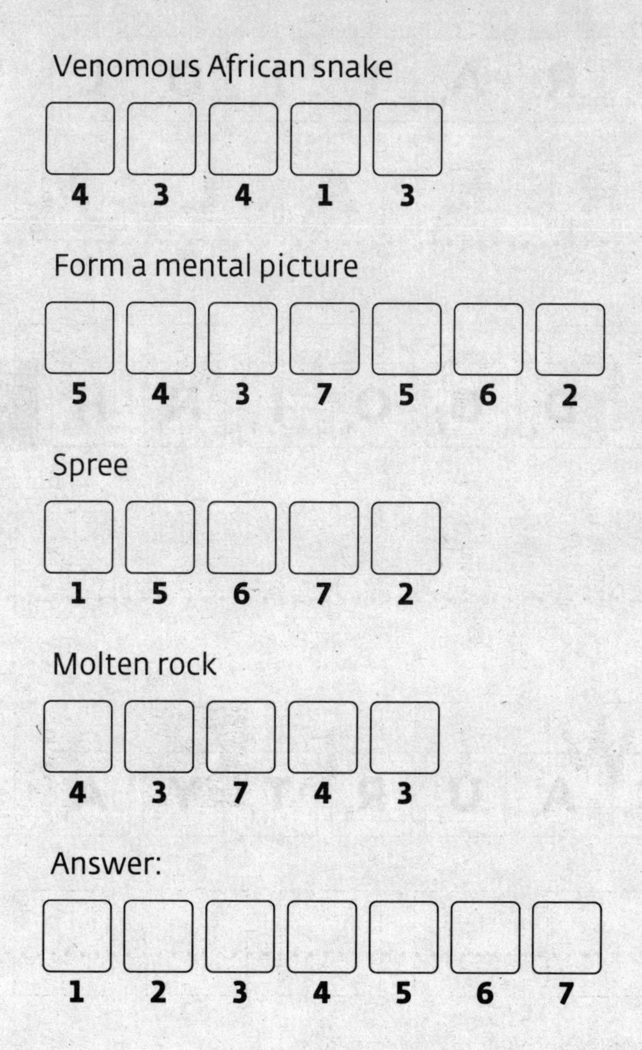

SCRABBLE™ Score

Make the highest score you can from each of the letter racks below. Add 50 points for a seven-letter word.

V4 R1 A1 I1 I1 O1 L1

....

L1 D2 G2 O1 I1 N1 H4

TRIPLE SCORE ON 5TH LETTER

....

C3 A1 U1 R1 T1 Y4 A1

....

Wordsearch

Can you find all of these gemstones from the Scrabble wordlist in the grid below? Words may appear horizontally, vertically or diagonally in either a forwards or backwards direction.

I	L	C	Q	J	L	Y	G	J	O	R	K	Y	C
A	M	E	T	H	Y	S	T	P	W	U	L	M	W
S	C	E	Z	H	S	W	A	Q	V	B	S	T	A
H	R	M	N	B	K	L	A	K	J	Y	S	X	S
X	E	E	D	I	Q	N	A	I	D	I	S	B	O
E	Y	T	N	I	R	J	Z	L	J	A	D	E	R
T	R	N	I	O	A	A	Z	T	R	A	U	Q	Z
O	J	I	O	H	T	M	M	B	J	A	U	Z	F
D	E	A	H	K	C	S	O	A	I	W	E	B	D
I	F	A	S	P	Z	A	N	N	U	Y	A	P	T
R	V	D	W	P	P	W	L	U	D	Q	X	T	O
E	Z	F	D	X	E	A	N	A	S	Y	A	P	P
P	A	M	B	E	R	R	S	V	M	L	J	G	A
R	M	L	E	N	I	P	S	W	G	J	X	Q	Z

AMBER
AMETHYST
AQUAMARINE
DIAMOND
JADE
JASPER
MALACHITE
OBSIDIAN
ONYX
OPAL
PEARL
PERIDOT
QUARTZ
RUBY
SAPPHIRE
SPINEL
SUNSTONE
TOPAZ

Give Me a Clue

Can you fill-in the blank tiles to create a word that solves each of the clues below?

Plot secretly

_ C _ _ M _

Spanish soup

G _ _ P _ _ H O

Paste made from almonds

_ A _ Z _ _ A _

Whirlwind

T _ _ _ _ D _

Anagrams

Can you find the word that can be made from the following letters?

ODTREAME

....

Can you find the two words that can be made from the following letters?

ELTIATC

....

....

Can you find the three words that can be made from the following letters?

LIKNS

....

....

....

Themed Anagrams

Can you crack these anagrams of cosmetics?

CLIP KITS

....

ONCE CLEAR

....

WEEDS AHOY

....

MR RIPE

....

Word Wheel

Find as many words of 4+ letters as you can, using the letters in the wheel. All words must use the central letter. One word will use all the letters in the wheel.

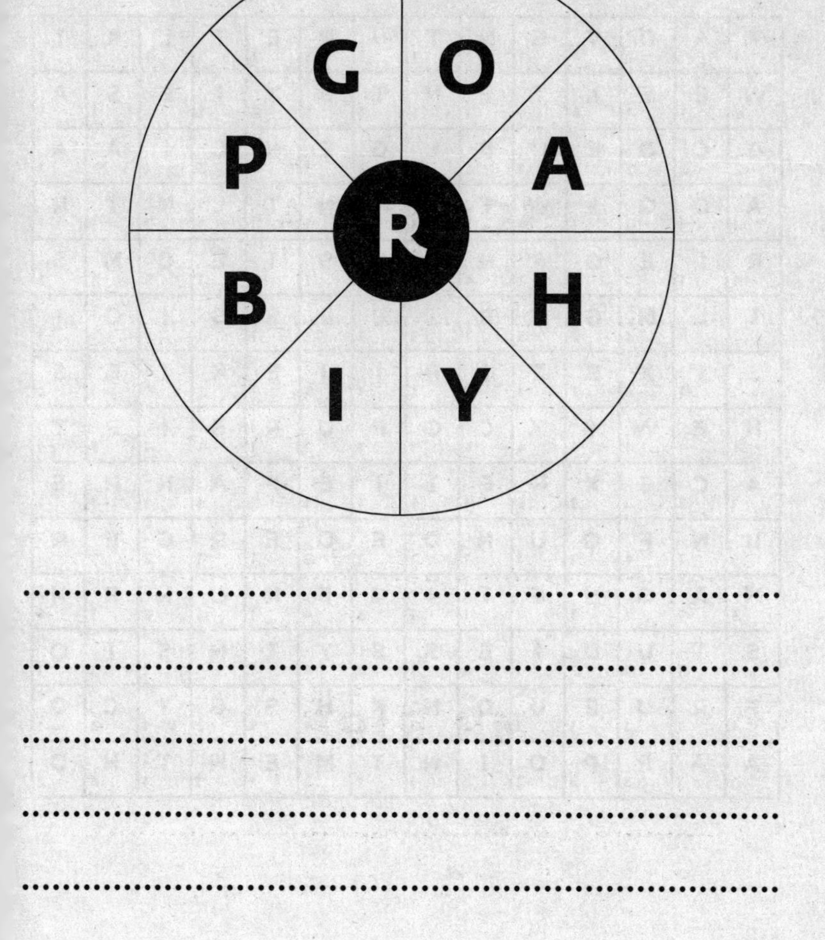

SCRABBLE™ Soup

Find the highest-scoring word you can in the grid of letters below by summing the values assigned to each letter tile in your word: for instance the word EXAMPLE would score 18 points. Words may appear horizontally, vertically or diagonally in the grid, and in either a forwards or backwards direction.

T 1	A 1	D 2	V 4	E 1	N 1	T 1	U 1	R 1	E 1	T 1	L 1	K 5	T 1
W 4	E 1	E 1	X 8	T 1	E 1	N 1	T 1	S 1	X 8	I 1	E 1	S 1	A 1
G 2	C 3	Q 10	E 1	U 1	F 4	L 1	G 2	E 1	N 1	C 3	I 1	A 1	A 1
A 1	O 1	Q 10	I 1	W 4	T 1	E 1	M 3	N 1	T 1	L 1	N 1	T 1	R 1
R 1	L 1	E 1	G 2	A 1	H 4	A 1	E 1	S 1	I 1	E 1	C 3	M 3	S 1
I 1	L 1	M 3	G 2	C 3	R 1	T 1	B 3	R 1	S 1	S 1	I 1	O 1	I 1
S 1	I 1	X 8	B 3	E 1	I 1	R 1	I 1	J 8	E 1	K 5	T 1	S 1	S 1
H 4	E 1	W 4	I 1	Y 4	C 3	O 1	R 1	U 1	R 1	S 1	I 1	P 3	T 1
A 1	C 3	S 1	X 8	K 5	E 1	T 1	I 1	E 1	P 3	A 1	N 1	H 4	E 1
U 1	N 1	F 4	O 1	U 1	N 1	D 2	E 1	D 2	E 1	R 1	G 2	E 1	R 1
M 3	A 1	G 2	N 1	E 1	T 1	I 1	C 3	F 4	N 1	O 1	H 4	R 1	H 4
S 1	T 1	U 1	D 2	I 1	E 1	S 1	S 1	Y 4	T 1	N 1	S 1	I 1	O 1
F 4	R 1	U 1	E 1	U 1	D 2	N 1	K 5	H 4	S 1	G 2	T 1	C 3	O 1
A 1	A 1	P 3	P 3	O 1	I 1	N 1	T 1	M 3	E 1	N 1	T 1	H 4	D 2

Word Ladder

Use each of the tiles once to move from the word at the top of the ladder to the word at the bottom. You may only change one letter on each rung of the ladder, and must make a valid word on each rung. Use each of the Scrabble tiles once to do so.

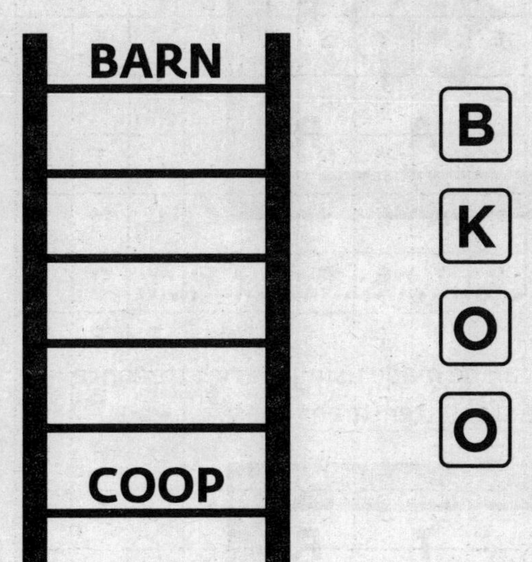

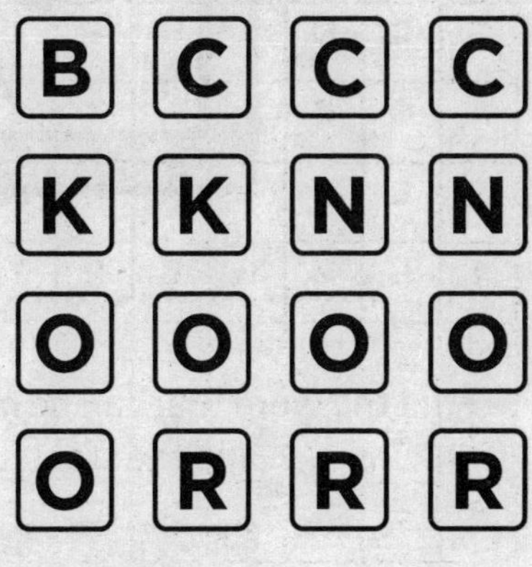

Star Letter

Find the word that can be made using every letter once, and the star letter twice.

Find the word that can be made using every letter once, and the star letter three times.

Consonant Crossword

Complete the crossword puzzle, in which all the vowels have already been placed. You must use each consonant tile listed once to fill the grid.

Word Splits

Can you combine the word segments below to make three words?

ANS TR IBE CR

....

NO MO NY US SY

....

DSC ED AP LAN

....

Link Words

Find the word that can replace the question marks on each line to make two new words or phrases. Use each of the Scrabble tiles once to do so.

SKETCH ???? MARK

HEAD ???? WIDTH

SIGN ???? DATE

A B B D

K N O O

O P S T

Missing Vowels

All the vowels have been removed from three words. Use each of the vowel tiles below once to reconstruct the words.

1) CHSV

2) PHVL

3) TMC

A A A E

E E I I

O O U

Word Square

Use the Scrabble tiles provided to fill the grid, so that the answer to each crossword clue appears in the corresponding row of the grid. Once complete, the same answer words will also appear in the columns.

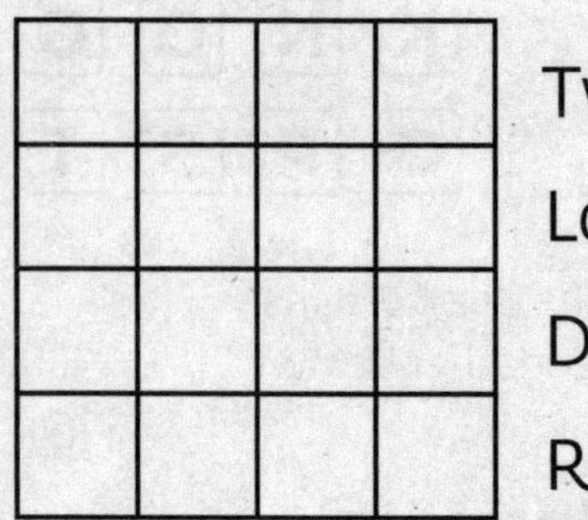

Type of golf club

Loose flowing garment

Double-reed instrument

Require

B B D E

E E E I

N N O O

O O R R

Unscramble

Can you unscramble the two insects that have been mixed together below?

DECKCHAIR TIP

....

....

Can you unscramble the three organs that have been mixed together below?

NATURAL HERB GIN

....

....

....

Word Slider

Move each of the sliders up and down in order to form six-letter words in the middle row. Can you find five-or-more words?

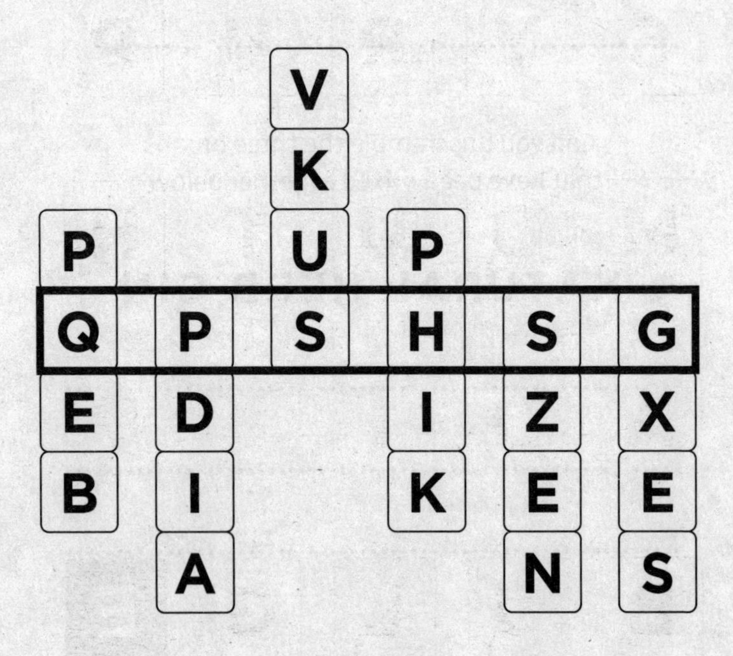

SCRABBLE™ Word

Can you guess the SCRABBLE™ Word? It is a word found in the Scrabble dictionary that does not repeat any letters. In each of the guesses below, a white background means the letter does not appear in the answer word. A black background means a letter is both found in the word and is in the correct position, whilst a grey background means a letter is found in the answer word, but in a different position.

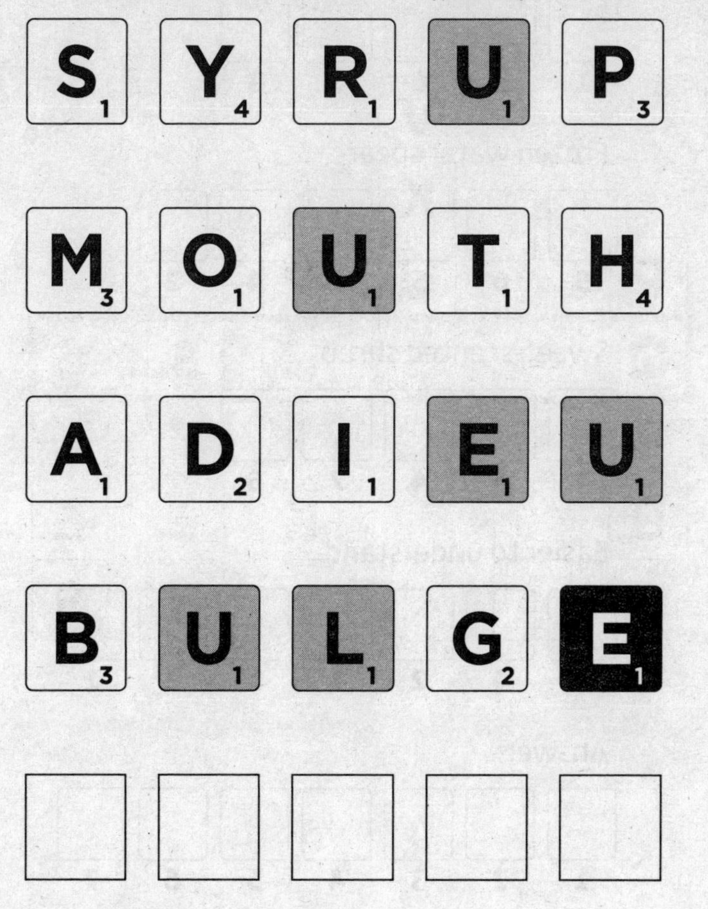

Value of solution tiles: 7 points

Seven Letters

A word composed of seven different letters has been created using Scrabble tiles. Can you answer the clues below to work out what that word is? Numbers indicate the position of each letter in the answer word.

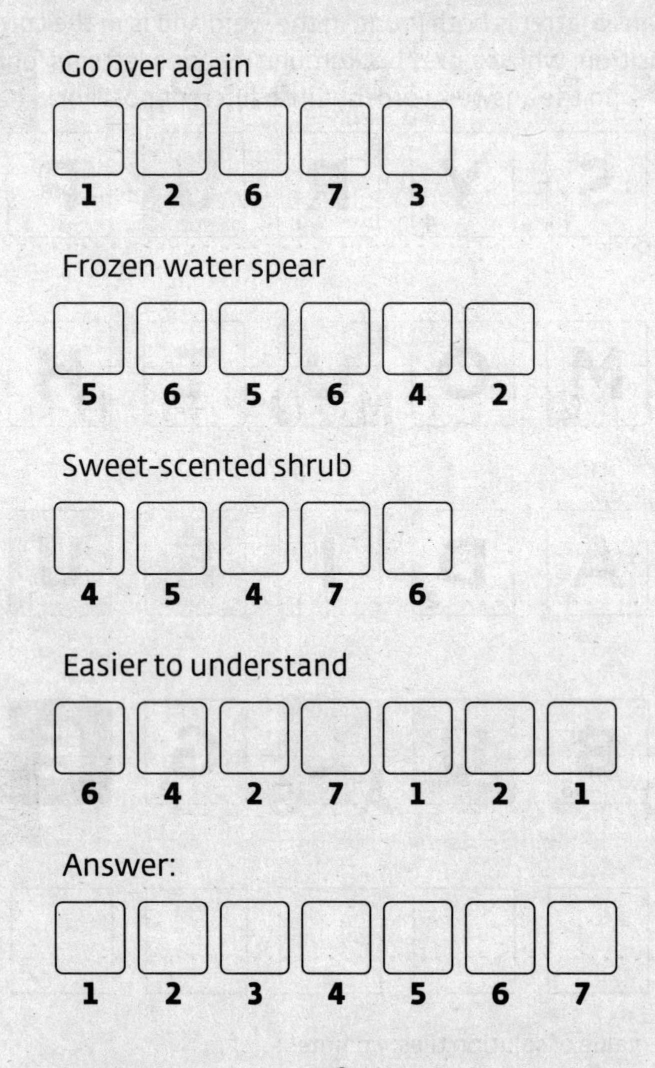

SCRABBLE™ Score

Make the highest score you can from each of the letter racks below. Add 50 points for a seven-letter word.

R 1 | N 1 | K 5 | S 1 | X 8 | D 2 | I 1 | TRIPLE WORD SCORE

R 1 | Q 10 | E 1 | M 3 | J 8 | P 3 | U 1

O 1 | U 1 | E 1 | A 1 | S 1 | L 1 | Z 10 | DOUBLE SCORE ON 7TH LETTER

Wordsearch

Can you find all of these words relating to happiness from the Scrabble wordlist in the grid below? Words may appear horizontally, vertically or diagonally in either a forwards or backwards direction.

M	E	P	L	U	F	R	E	E	H	C	C	T	X
L	H	E	F	X	U	K	D	G	N	I	K	O	J
U	T	L	E	T	H	R	I	L	L	E	D	E	P
F	I	B	S	X	D	E	T	A	L	E	F	D	Y
E	L	M	G	L	O	W	I	N	G	B	B	T	A
E	B	B	W	S	D	L	E	E	R	U	D	G	B
L	X	H	E	Y	U	E	Q	A	U	O	E	R	L
G	G	U	R	A	R	N	D	V	C	Y	L	A	O
X	X	R	B	F	M	I	N	B	O	A	I	T	C
X	E	W	E	E	A	I	L	Y	N	N	G	I	Y
M	K	R	X	N	R	X	N	K	T	T	H	F	L
V	A	J	T	X	Q	A	U	G	E	O	T	I	L
C	N	G	Y	A	L	E	N	B	N	F	E	E	O
S	T	Q	W	D	O	R	X	T	T	X	D	D	J

BEAMING
BLITHE
BUOYANT
CAREFREE
CHEERFUL
CONTENT
DELIGHTED
ELATED
EXUBERANT
GLEEFUL
GLOWING
GRATIFIED
JOKING
JOLLY
MERRY
RADIANT
SUNNY
THRILLED

Give Me a Clue

Can you fill-in the blank tiles to create a word that solves each of the clues below?

Non-professional

	M				U	

Account of the past

	E		O		

Willing to wait

P				E		

A person's vocabulary

	E			C		

Anagrams

Can you find the word that can be made from the following letters?

NRPNETTEI

....

Can you find the two words that can be made from the following letters?

NRGAOITS

....

....

Can you find the three words that can be made from the following letters?

OEEBSRV

....

....

....

Themed Anagrams

Can you crack these anagrams of animals?

COOL CIDER

....

ROOT SITE

....

UPPER ICON

....

STAR MEMO

....

Word Wheel

Find as many words of 4+ letters as you can, using the letters in the wheel. All words must use the central letter. One word will use all the letters in the wheel.

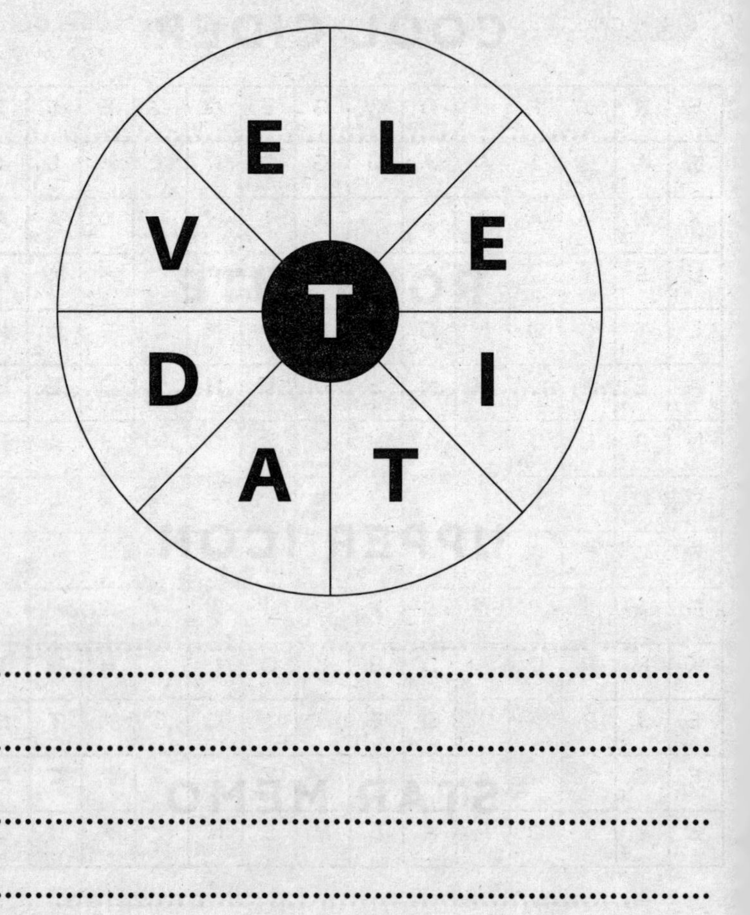

SCRABBLE™ Soup

Find the highest-scoring word you can in the grid of letters below by summing the values assigned to each letter tile in your word: for instance the word EXAMPLE would score 18 points. Words may appear horizontally, vertically or diagonally in the grid, and in either a forwards or backwards direction.

E 1	H 4	J 8	F 4	U 1	Q 10	W 4	G 2	E 1	Q 10	O 1	E 1	S 1	T 1
M 3	A 1	Q 10	L 1	R 1	A 1	U 1	G 2	O 1	R 1	I 1	L 1	L 1	A 1
X 8	M 3	P 3	A 1	B 3	S 1	T 1	A 1	I 1	N 1	E 1	D 2	A 1	A 1
U 1	S 1	I 1	V 4	V 4	A 1	I 1	L 1	U 1	P 3	C 3	H 4	W 4	N 1
L 1	T 1	C 3	O 1	N 1	C 3	E 1	P 3	T 1	N 1	U 1	E 1	D 2	N 1
A 1	E 1	P 3	L 1	U 1	M 3	E 1	D 2	V 4	U 1	T 1	P 3	E 1	U 1
N 1	R 1	L 1	J 8	I 1	A 1	N 1	C 3	H 4	O 1	R 1	S 1	A 1	L 1
D 2	M 3	I 1	L 1	L 1	I 1	O 1	N 1	L 1	P 3	N 1	S 1	L 1	M 3
E 1	C 3	O 1	R 1	D 2	I 1	A 1	L 1	A 1	E 1	N 1	D 2	I 1	E 1
D 2	A 1	L 1	T 1	S 1	B 3	I 1	O 1	J 8	A 1	W 4	B 3	N 1	N 1
K 5	R 1	R 1	O 1	A 1	D 2	B 3	L 1	O 1	C 3	K 5	N 1	G 2	T 1
E 1	J 8	R 1	A 1	T 1	D 2	E 1	S 1	I 1	C 3	C 3	A 1	T 1	E 1
E 1	S 1	Q 10	U 1	A 1	L 1	L 1	O 1	Z 10	I 1	U 1	P 3	C 3	A 1
E 1	Y 4	R 1	O 1	R 1	R 1	E 1	S 1	E 1	N 1	T 1	F 4	U 1	L 1

Word Ladder

Use each of the tiles once to move from the word at the top of the ladder to the word at the bottom. You may only change one letter on each rung of the ladder, and must make a valid word on each rung. Use each of the Scrabble tiles once to do so.

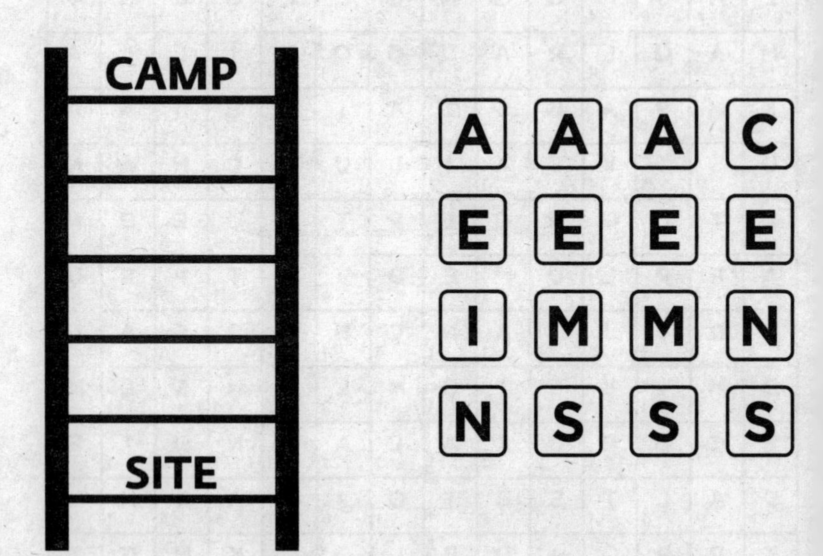

Star Letter

Find the word that can be made using every letter once, and the star letter twice.

....

Find the word that can be made using every letter once, and the star letter three times.

....

Consonant Crossword

Complete the crossword puzzle, in which all the vowels have already been placed. You must use each consonant tile listed once to fill the grid.

Word Splits

Can you combine the word segments
below to make three words?

AL RHE IC TOR

....

RAL DU PR OCE

....

ES PR EN CI CE

....

Link Words

Find the word that can replace the question marks on each line to make two new words or phrases. Use each of the Scrabble tiles once to do so.

WISE ????? DOWN

SHOOTING ???? FISH

FRIEND ???? MATE

A A C C

H I K P

R R S S

T

Missing Vowels

All the vowels have been removed from three words. Use each of the vowel tiles below once to reconstruct the words.

1) SMHW

2) RWG

3) NWHR

A E E

E E I

O O O

Word Square

Use the Scrabble tiles provided to fill the grid, so that the answer to each crossword clue appears in the corresponding row of the grid. Once complete, the same answer words will also appear in the columns.

Small quantity

Burden

Long pointed tooth

Requests

T T U U

Unscramble

Can you unscramble the two fashion accessories that have been mixed together below?

A BANAL TIGER

....

....

Can you unscramble the three types of nut that have been mixed together below?

LEAN PRAWN ACCOUNT

....

....

....

Word Slider

Move each of the sliders up and down in order to form six-letter words in the middle row. Can you find five-or-more words?

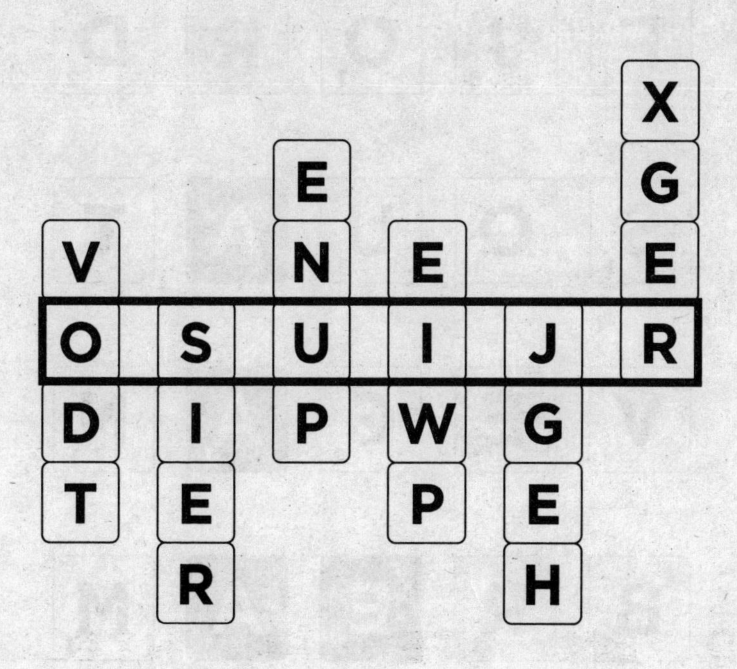

SCRABBLE™ Word

Can you guess the SCRABBLE™ Word? It is a word found in the Scrabble dictionary that does not repeat any letters. In each of the guesses below, a white background means the letter does not appear in the answer word. A black background means a letter is both found in the word and is in the correct position, whilst a grey background means a letter is found in the answer word, but in a different position.

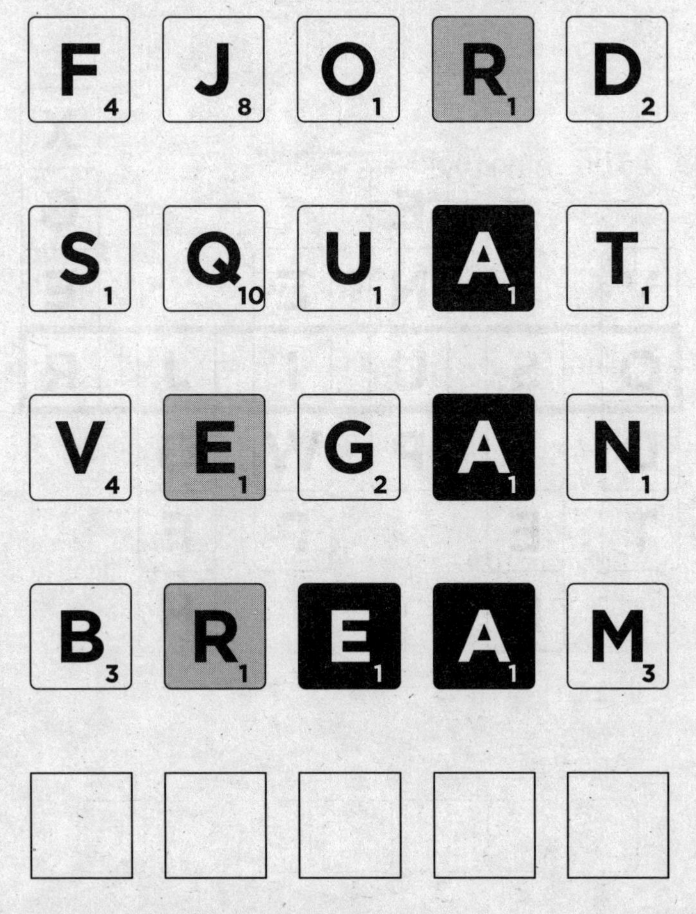

Value of solution tiles: 7 points

Seven Letters

A word composed of seven different letters has been created using Scrabble tiles. Can you answer the clues below to work out what that word is? Numbers indicate the position of each letter in the answer word.

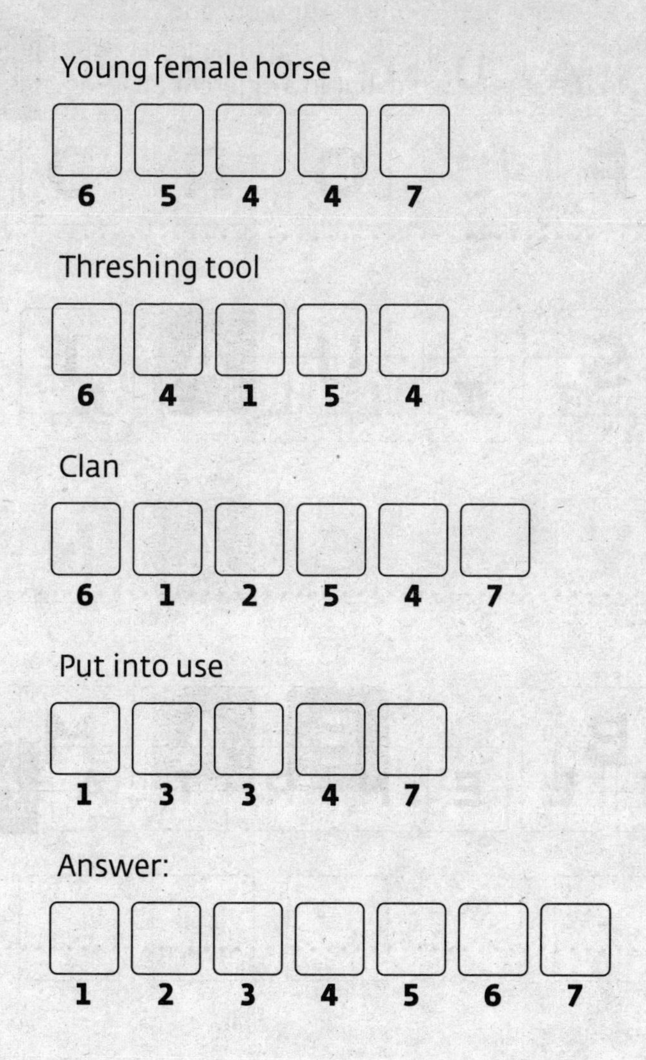

SCRABBLE™ Score

Make the highest score you can from each of the letter racks below. Add 50 points for a seven-letter word.

K 5	A 1	U 1	Q 10	C 3	W 4	S 1	TRIPLE SCORE ON 2ND LETTER

....

E 1	T 1	T 1	I 1	L 1	E 1	X 8

....

N 1	L 1	E 1	N 1	R 1	T 1	A 1	TRIPLE WORD SCORE

....

Wordsearch

Can you find all of these herbal tea flavours from the Scrabble wordlist in the grid below? Words may appear horizontally, vertically or diagonally in either a forwards or backwards direction.

H	T	T	K	B	M	M	L	H	A	D	B	M	A
G	Z	N	B	U	N	V	L	I	T	N	T	N	E
K	Q	M	D	R	R	T	I	B	Y	R	F	S	J
S	A	Y	N	D	O	C	D	I	T	E	O	P	F
S	N	X	O	O	H	N	O	S	W	R	S	S	V
O	O	C	M	C	T	E	T	C	Z	G	K	A	T
B	M	E	L	K	W	T	V	U	O	C	B	G	C
I	A	W	A	Z	A	T	A	S	A	N	F	E	G
O	N	P	H	Z	H	L	Z	R	N	E	U	I	L
O	N	A	G	U	P	E	D	M	N	E	N	T	I
R	I	P	A	U	K	A	H	N	D	S	L	I	M
B	C	A	W	L	M	W	E	Q	E	G	L	V	E
P	S	Y	D	O	M	L	L	N	E	L	P	P	A
M	F	A	M	G	I	N	G	E	R	S	I	C	W

ALMOND
APPLE
BURDOCK
CARDAMOM
CINNAMON
COCONUT
DILL
FENNEL
GINGER
GINSENG
HAWTHORN
HIBISCUS
LIME
NETTLE
PAPAYA
ROOIBOS
ROSE
SAGE

Give Me a Clue

Can you fill-in the blank tiles to create a word that solves each of the clues below?

Customer

C _ _ _ _ T

Plan of action

_ T _ _ T _ _ Y

Snowstorm

B _ _ _ _ A _ D

Obvious

P _ T _ _ _

Anagrams

Can you find the word that can be made
from the following letters?

ASDHWINC

....

Can you find the two words that can be
made from the following letters?

EEPUMSR

....

....

Can you find the three words that can be
made from the following letters?

ETRVO

....

....

....

Themed Anagrams

Can you crack these anagrams relating to hiking?

HAD MAPLE

....

DENSE SWIRL

....

OAF TOWER

....

INVENTOR MEN

....

Word Wheel

Find as many words of 4+ letters as you can, using the letters in the wheel. All words must use the central letter. One word will use all the letters in the wheel.

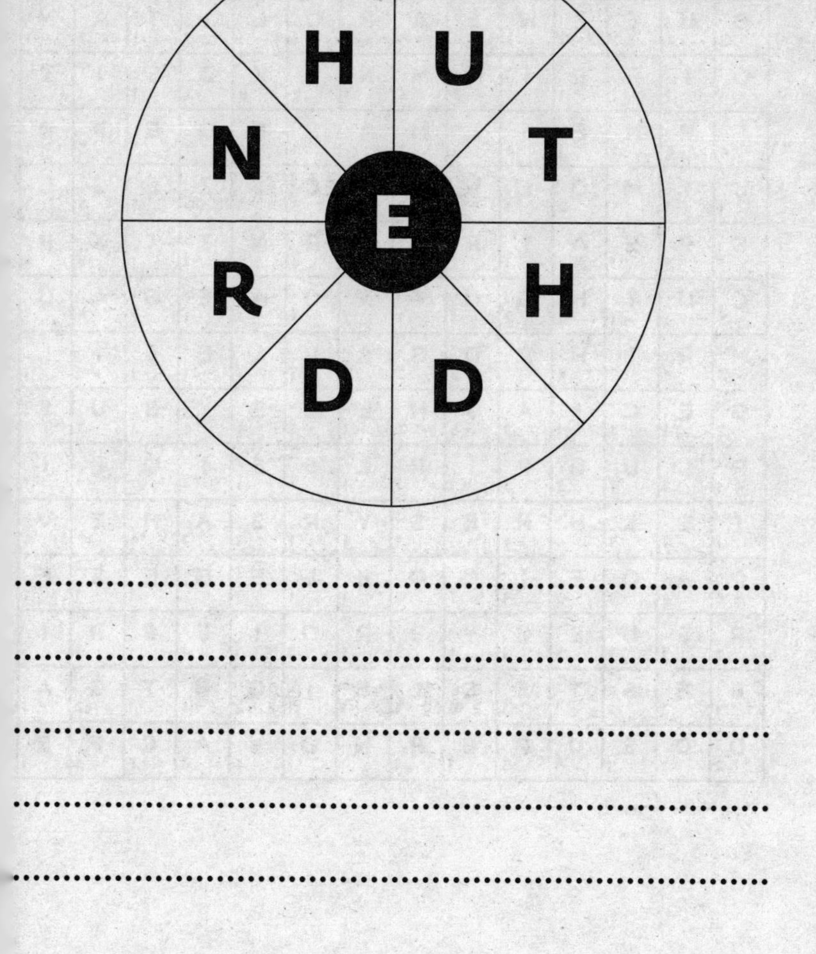

SCRABBLE™ Soup

Find the highest-scoring word you can in the grid of letters below by summing the values assigned to each letter tile in your word: for instance the word EXAMPLE would score 18 points. Words may appear horizontally, vertically or diagonally in the grid, and in either a forwards or backwards direction.

B 3	U 1	I 1	Z 10	N 1	E 1	A 1	P 3	O 1	L 1	I 1	T 1	A 1	N 1
O 1	I 1	E 1	E 1	I 1	M 3	M 3	N 1	G 2	X 8	D 2	S 1	I 1	T 1
F 4	H 4	N 1	E 1	J 8	L 1	M 3	A 1	S 1	F 4	O 1	E 1	P 3	R 1
U 1	T 1	M 3	D 2	E 1	U 1	U 1	T 1	C 3	I 1	Z 10	E 1	S 1	E 1
S 1	P 3	E 1	A 1	I 1	R 1	U 1	U 1	R 1	N 1	T 1	T 1	X 8	P 3
C 3	U 1	T 1	H 4	G 2	N 1	T 1	R 1	O 1	A 1	E 1	G 2	A 1	U 1
M 3	R 1	I 1	H 4	R 1	D 2	G 2	A 1	L 1	L 1	E 1	S 1	I 1	L 1
G 2	E 1	C 3	I 1	A 1	J 8	M 3	L 1	L 1	E 1	Y 4	B 3	U 1	S 1
R 1	L 1	U 1	G 2	P 3	I 1	R 1	L 1	S 1	S 1	I 1	Q 10	L 1	I 1
I 1	E 1	L 1	H 4	H 4	E 1	S 1	Y 4	R 1	S 1	A 1	H 4	Z 10	V 4
P 3	A 1	O 1	E 1	I 1	C 3	O 1	L 1	L 1	E 1	G 2	E 1	S 1	E 1
P 3	S 1	U 1	S 1	C 3	Y 4	B 3	R 1	O 1	I 1	L 1	E 1	R 1	I 1
E 1	E 1	S 1	T 1	S 1	S 1	L 1	E 1	I 1	G 2	H 4	T 1	G 2	A 1
D 2	D 2	S 1	U 1	P 3	E 1	R 1	N 1	O 1	V 4	A 1	C 3	F 4	E 1

Word Ladder

Use each of the tiles once to move from the word at the top of the ladder to the word at the bottom. You may only change one letter on each rung of the ladder, and must make a valid word on each rung. Use each of the Scrabble tiles once to do so.

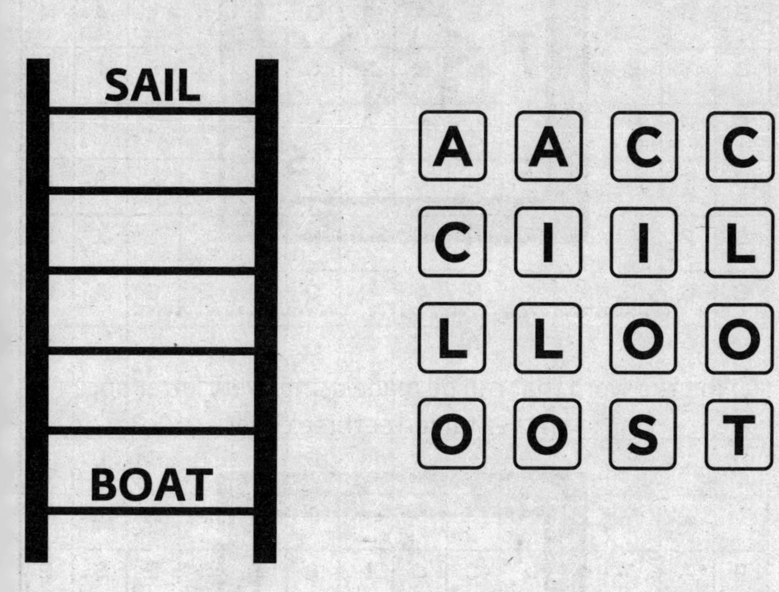

Star Letter

Find the word that can be made using every letter once, and the star letter twice.

Find the word that can be made using every letter once, and the star letter three times.

Consonant Crossword

Complete the crossword puzzle, in which all the vowels have already been placed. You must use each consonant tile listed once to fill the grid.

Word Splits

Can you combine the word segments below to make three words?

TI ERA ON IT

....

LIG NEG CE EN

....

RR NA IV ES AT

....

Link Words

Find the word that can replace the question marks on each line to make two new words or phrases. Use each of the Scrabble tiles once to do so.

HAND ??? PIPES

PENCIL ???? STUDY

LEMON ???? ANCHOR

A A B C

D E G O

P R S

Missing Vowels

All the vowels have been removed from three words. Use each of the vowel tiles below once to reconstruct the words.

1) HRC

2) VGLY

3) MDT

A A E E

E E I I

O U

Word Square

Use the Scrabble tiles provided to fill the grid, so that the answer to each crossword clue appears in the corresponding row of the grid. Once complete, the same answer words will also appear in the columns.

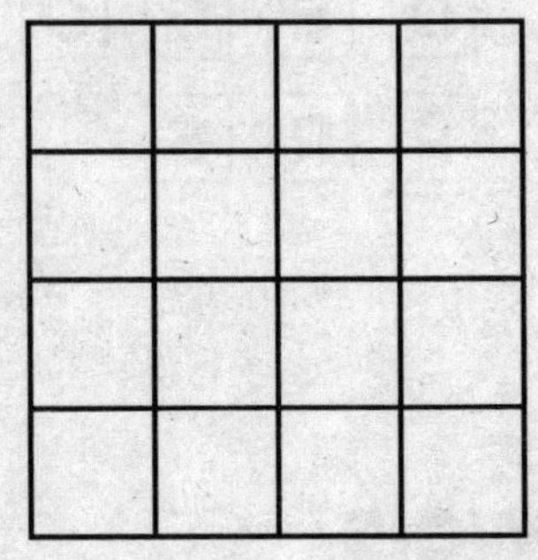

Boast

Rank

Basic unit of matter

Precious stones

Unscramble

Can you unscramble the two fruits that have been mixed together below?

NAG ATOMIC PRO

....

....

Can you unscramble the three nocturnal animals that have been mixed together below?

PUB MEAL ATOM

....

....

....

Word Slider

Move each of the sliders up and down in order to form six-letter words in the middle row. Can you find five-or-more words?

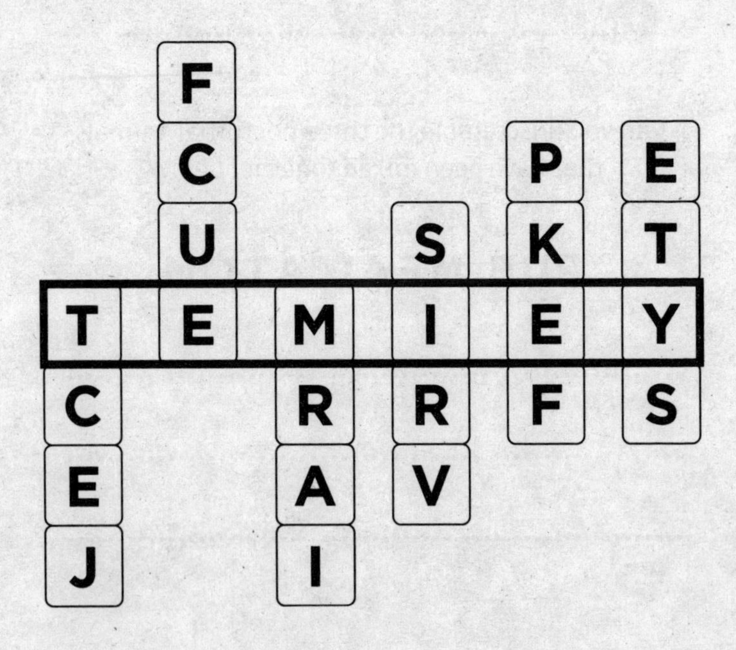

SCRABBLE™ Word

Can you guess the SCRABBLE™ Word? It is a word found in the Scrabble dictionary that does not repeat any letters. In each of the guesses below, a white background means the letter does not appear in the answer word. A black background means a letter is both found in the word and is in the correct position, whilst a grey background means a letter is found in the answer word, but in a different position.

Value of solution tiles: 7 points

Seven Letters

A word composed of seven different letters has been created using Scrabble tiles. Can you answer the clues below to work out what that word is? Numbers indicate the position of each letter in the answer word.

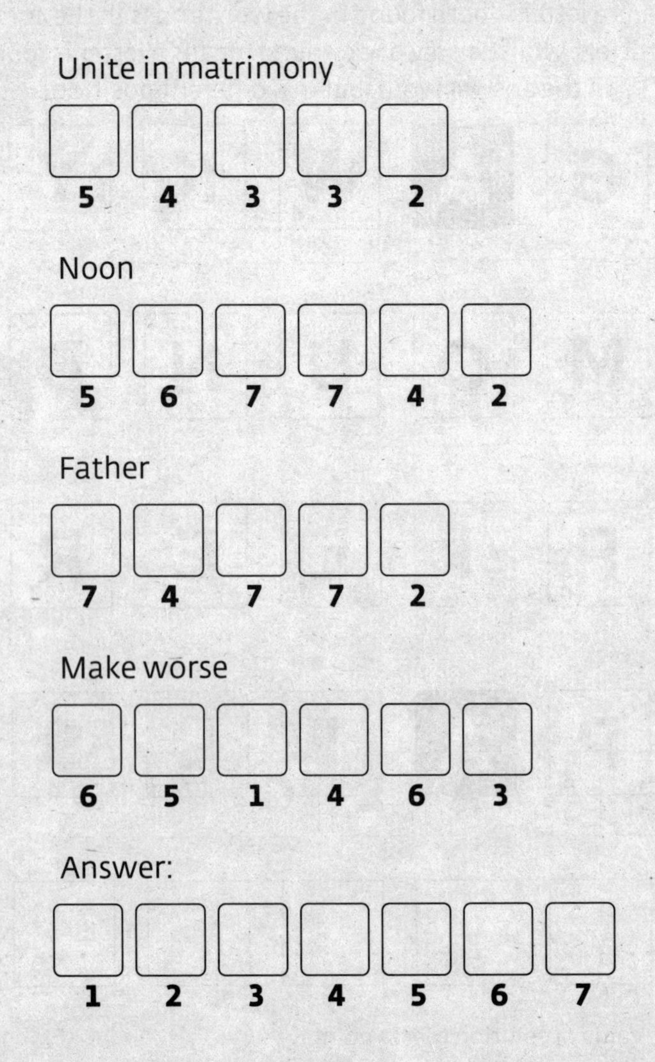

SCRABBLE™ Score

Make the highest score you can from each of the letter racks below. Add 50 points for a seven-letter word.

R1 D2 A1 I1 O1 N1 D2 — DOUBLE WORD SCORE

B3 A1 H4 C3 D2 E1 R1 — DOUBLE SCORE ON 6TH LETTER

R1 N1 A1 L1 G2 A1 D2

Wordsearch

Can you find all of these words relating to creative writing from the Scrabble wordlist in the grid below? Words may appear horizontally, vertically or diagonally in either a forwards or backwards direction.

```
H L E Y I P O E T R Y D F C
M E R R J D F I C T I O N P
N V U D T R S R W H O X Q G
V O T X P U R M V V Y N L N
X N A Z L E N E C S E O E I
S W R J O R O H T U A P C T
N D E F T U S X P U Z X A T
N I T C H A R A C T E R P E
T A I W P P E M L Z C U S S
I L L A L L R I O M E M L Q
C O H A Y U Q G Z Z O L P S
H G Y T D Z W W B D R A M A
G U S X A C T I O N T E K V
S E I E S U S P E N S E C L
```

ACTION	PACE
AUTHOR	PLAY
CHARACTER	PLOT
DIALOGUE	POETRY
DRAMA	SCENE
FICTION	SETTING
LITERATURE	STYLE
MEMOIR	SUSPENSE
NOVEL	TONE

Give Me a Clue

Can you fill-in the blank tiles to create a word that solves each of the clues below?

Old World monkey

	A			Q		

Ballroom dance

F					O	

Computers

	A			W			E

Wreath of flowers

	A		L			

Anagrams

Can you find the word that can be made from the following letters?

EAUPVNSRO

....

Can you find the two words that can be made from the following letters?

ISAYTLRO

....

....

Can you find the three words that can be made from the following letters?

SRESVE

....

....

....

Themed Anagrams

Can you crack these anagrams of vegetables?

ACTOR HIKE

....

AWFUL RECOIL

....

RIP PANS

....

HIP SCAN

....

Word Wheel

Find as many words of 4+ letters as you can, using the letters in the wheel. All words must use the central letter. One word will use all the letters in the wheel.

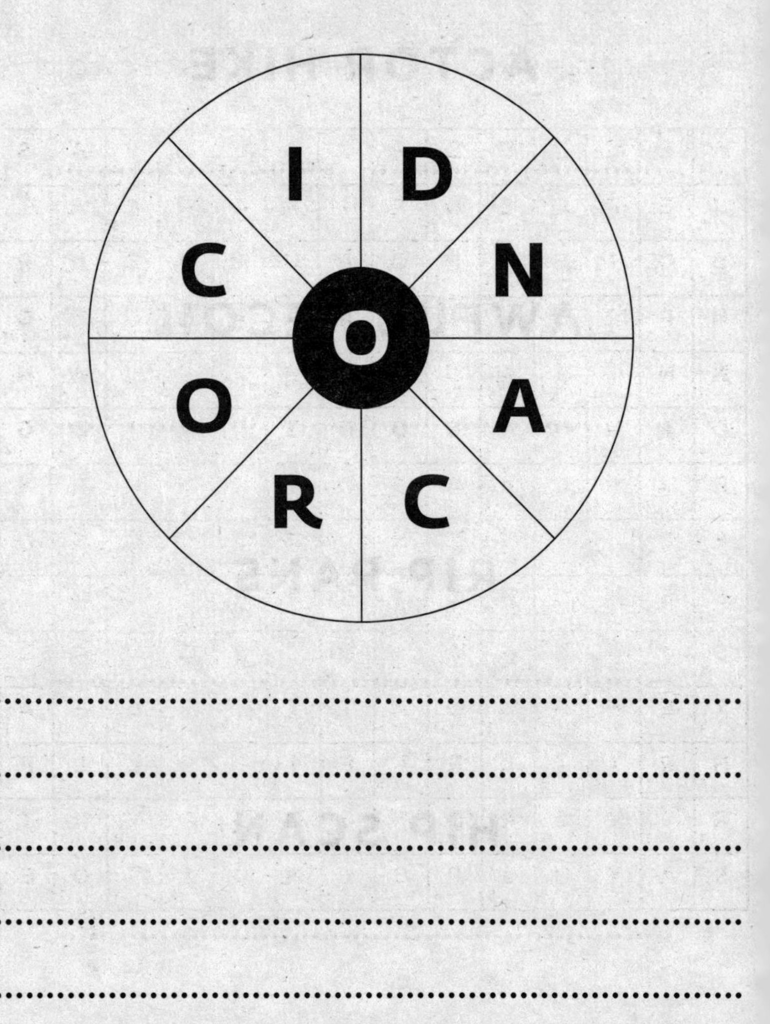

SCRABBLE™ Soup

Find the highest-scoring word you can in the grid of letters below by summing the values assigned to each letter tile in your word: for instance the word EXAMPLE would score 18 points. Words may appear horizontally, vertically or diagonally in the grid, and in either a forwards or backwards direction.

W 4	E 1	E 1	D 2	E 1	D 2	P 3	J 8	A 1	C 3	G 2	V 4	A 1	S 1
J 8	E 1	R 1	D 2	E 1	N 1	R 1	I 1	X 8	O 1	R 1	C 3	A 1	T 1
B 3	O 1	I 1	C 3	R 1	P 3	O 1	A 1	U 1	M 3	K 5	O 1	R 1	R 1
U 1	P 3	R 1	O 1	L 1	I 1	V 4	R 1	A 1	P 3	N 1	N 1	T 1	O 1
N 1	N 1	I 1	I 1	W 4	U 1	I 1	D 2	B 3	A 1	U 1	V 4	W 4	N 1
D 2	A 1	N 1	N 1	R 1	B 3	D 2	R 1	S 1	R 1	T 1	I 1	O 1	G 2
R 1	J 8	H 4	C 3	A 1	U 1	E 1	O 1	T 1	E 1	M 3	N 1	R 1	H 4
E 1	E 1	U 1	I 1	T 1	Z 10	N 1	U 1	R 1	S 1	E 1	C 3	K 5	O 1
S 1	S 1	M 3	D 2	H 4	Z 10	T 1	G 2	A 1	R 1	G 2	I 1	V 4	L 1
S 1	T 1	A 1	E 1	F 4	W 4	I 1	H 4	C 3	S 1	W 4	N 1	A 1	D 2
T 1	E 1	N 1	N 1	U 1	O 1	A 1	T 1	T 1	M 3	T 1	G 2	E 1	A 1
H 4	R 1	I 1	T 1	L 1	R 1	L 1	E 1	I 1	R 1	O 1	L 1	L 1	P 3
R 1	S 1	T 1	S 1	R 1	D 2	F 4	L 1	O 1	E 1	O 1	Y 4	K 5	T 1
S 1	A 1	Y 4	U 1	J 8	P 3	B 3	L 1	N 1	D 2	I 1	S 1	O 1	E 1

Word Ladder

Use each of the tiles once to move from the word at the top of the ladder to the word at the bottom. You may only change one letter on each rung of the ladder, and must make a valid word on each rung. Use each of the Scrabble tiles once to do so.

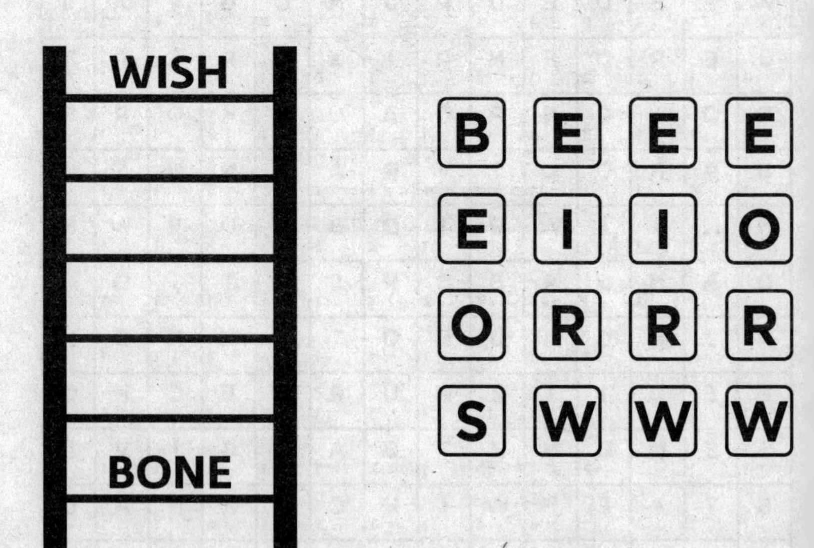

Star Letter

Find the word that can be made using every letter once, and the star letter twice.

....

Find the word that can be made using every letter once, and the star letter three times.

....

Consonant Crossword

Complete the crossword puzzle, in which all the vowels have already been placed. You must use each consonant tile listed once to fill the grid.

Word Splits

Can you combine the word segments below to make three words?

RS IVE ANN ARY

....

STI TU LE RN

....

COM IVE RAT PA

....

Link Words

Find the word that can replace the question marks on each line to make two new words or phrases. Use each of the Scrabble tiles once to do so.

PIE ????? TOPPER

ROCKING ????? LIFT

EVER ????? GROCER

A	A	C	C
E	E	G	H
H	I	N	R
R	R	T	

Missing Vowels

All the vowels have been removed from three words. Use each of the vowel tiles below once to reconstruct the words.

1) TBCC

2) WRFR

3) LGBK

A	A	A
E	O	O
O	O	O

Word Square

Use the Scrabble tiles provided to fill the grid, so that the answer to each crossword clue appears in the corresponding row of the grid. Once complete, the same answer words will also appear in the columns.

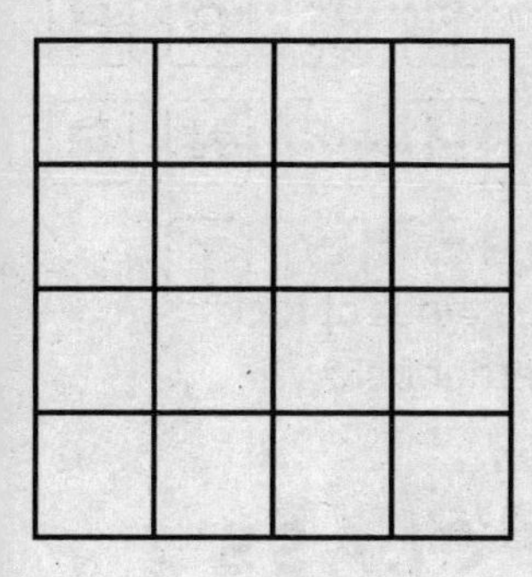

Zest; liveliness

Creative thought

Small amphibian

Movable barrier

T T W Z

Unscramble

Can you unscramble the two colours that have been mixed together below?

POPULAR GENRE

....

....

Can you unscramble the three types of rock that have been mixed together below?

KALE HEALTH CLASS

....

....

....

Word Slider

Move each of the sliders up and down in order to form six-letter words in the middle row. Can you find five-or-more words?

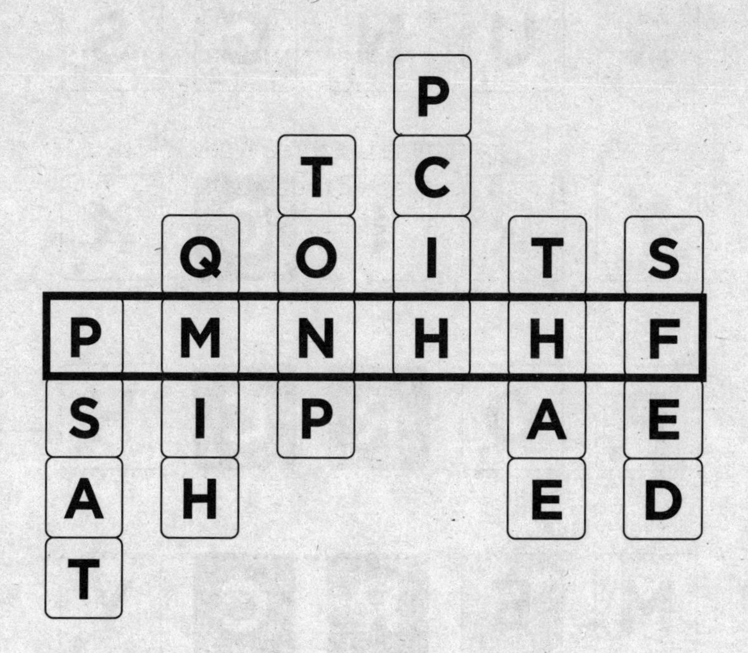

SCRABBLE™ Word

Can you guess the SCRABBLE™ Word? It is a word found in the Scrabble dictionary that does not repeat any letters. In each of the guesses below, a white background means the letter does not appear in the answer word. A black background means a letter is both found in the word and is in the correct position, whilst a grey background means a letter is found in the answer word, but in a different position.

Value of solution tiles: 10 points

Seven Letters

A word composed of seven different letters has been created using Scrabble tiles. Can you answer the clues below to work out what that word is? Numbers indicate the position of each letter in the answer word.

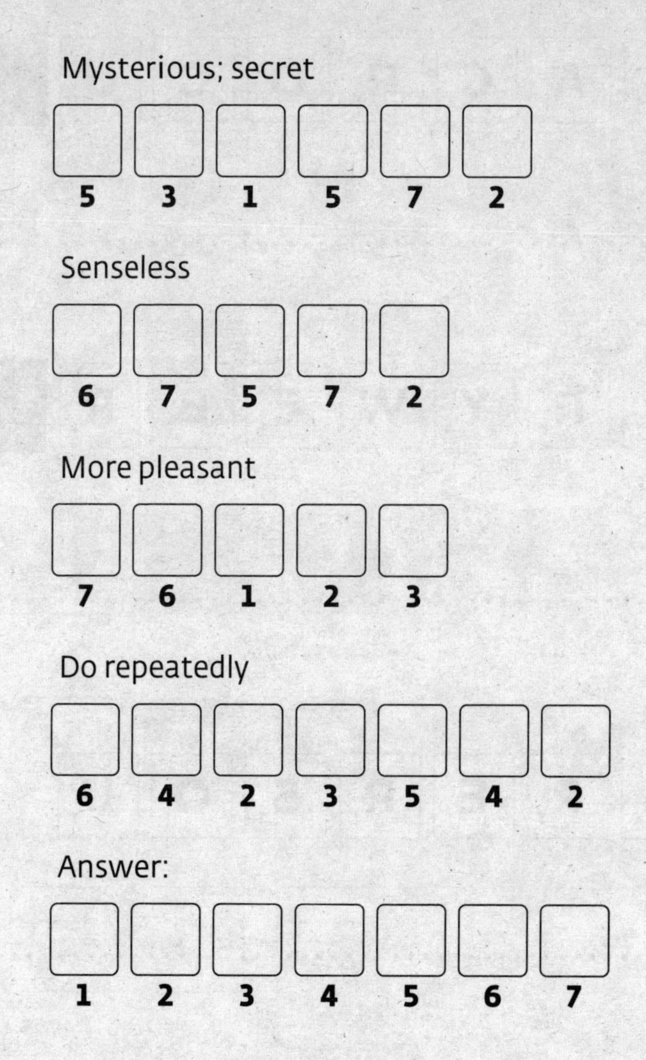

SCRABBLE™ Score

Make the highest score you can from each of the letter racks below. Add 50 points for a seven-letter word.

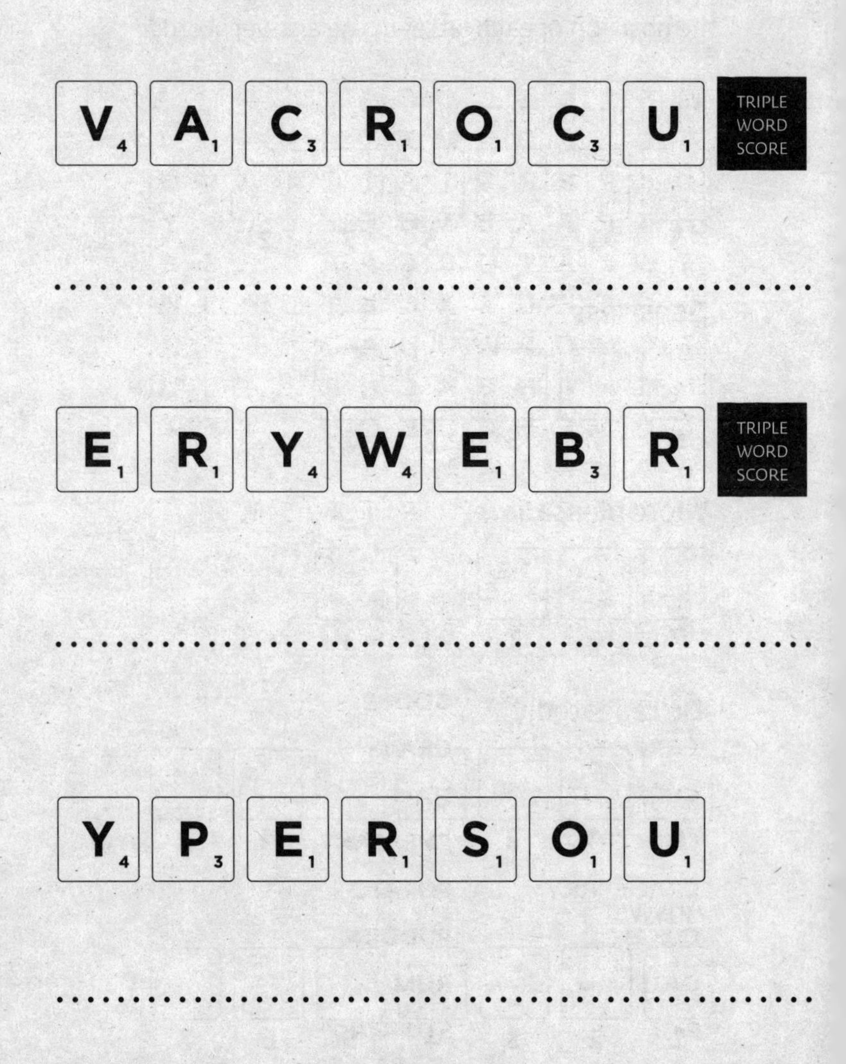

Wordsearch

Can you find all of these Christmas food and drink items from the Scrabble wordlist in the grid below? Words may appear horizontally, vertically or diagonally in either a forwards or backwards direction.

Z	S	Y	B	T	G	O	O	S	E	G	F	H	Q
T	D	X	R	Q	A	M	X	T	P	N	H	E	H
U	K	R	R	R	S	J	A	I	O	I	A	V	U
N	Z	R	A	A	E	L	O	E	T	D	M	X	Y
T	W	X	A	T	O	B	C	F	A	D	F	S	E
S	N	S	K	C	S	X	N	B	T	U	R	S	K
E	O	U	O	P	W	U	D	A	O	P	U	T	R
H	C	H	A	H	B	R	C	N	R	J	I	U	U
C	C	W	E	E	C	U	B	Q	U	C	T	F	T
B	P	M	F	A	A	M	R	R	U	K	C	F	G
P	L	E	C	S	R	D	A	T	E	S	A	I	O
S	E	M	K	A	R	V	S	G	I	F	K	N	F
B	H	F	K	N	O	Q	O	M	X	F	E	G	R
K	M	K	P	T	T	B	B	M	G	R	A	V	Y

BEEF

CARROT

CHESTNUT

CHOCOLATE

CRANBERRY

CUSTARD

DATES

FIGS

FRUITCAKE

GOOSE

GRAVY

HAM

PHEASANT

POTATO

PUDDING

RUM

STUFFING

TURKEY

Give Me a Clue

Can you fill-in the blank tiles to create a word that solves each of the clues below?

Small shop

	O				Q		E

Type of house

	U			A		O	

Type of painting

	O			R			T

Very strong or healthy

	O		U		

Anagrams

Can you find the word that can be made from the following letters?

UTTPRME

....

Can you find the two words that can be made from the following letters?

ATNSTTEME

....

....

Can you find the three words that can be made from the following letters?

SDETAK

....

....

....

Themed Anagrams

Can you crack these anagrams relating to travel?

MAT ORIGIN

....

COSY DRIVE

....

RELAX OPTION

....

LEAN OPERA

....

Word Wheel

Find as many words of 4+ letters as you can, using the letters in the wheel. All words must use the central letter. One word will use all the letters in the wheel.

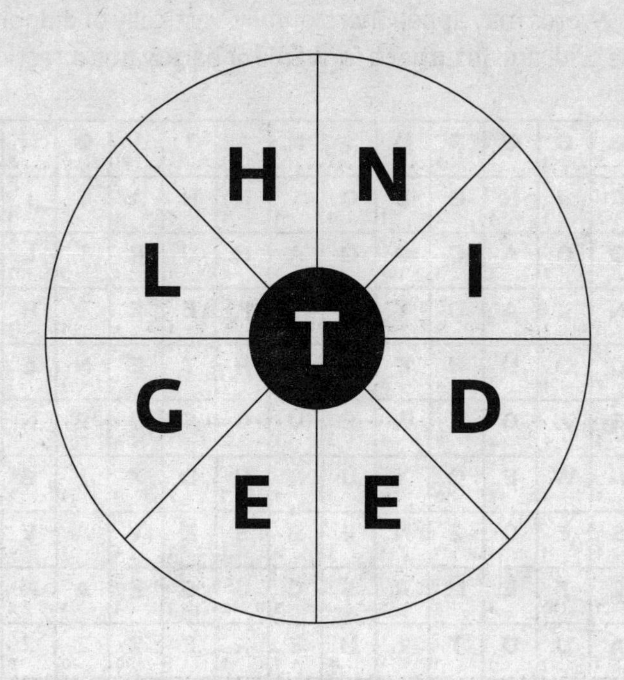

SCRABBLE™ Soup

Find the highest-scoring word you can in the grid of letters below by summing the values assigned to each letter tile in your word: for instance the word EXAMPLE would score 18 points. Words may appear horizontally, vertically or diagonally in the grid, and in either a forwards or backwards direction.

R 1	C 3	O 1	O 1	R 1	D 2	I 1	N 1	A 1	T 1	I 1	O 1	N 1	R 1
E 1	C 3	R 1	H 4	G 2	E 1	O 1	I 1	N 1	H 4	A 1	B 3	I 1	T 1
U 1	O 1	D 2	A 1	C 3	Q 10	Q 10	A 1	H 4	U 1	R 1	T 1	L 1	E 1
I 1	N 1	L 1	A 1	D 2	Y 4	L 1	I 1	K 5	E 1	E 1	R 1	R 1	J 8
N 1	D 2	O 1	U 1	H 4	E 1	I 1	G 2	H 4	T 1	E 1	N 1	E 1	U 1
D 2	E 1	W 4	G 2	X 8	W 4	E 1	U 1	G 2	S 1	J 8	E 1	N 1	B 3
I 1	N 1	W 4	E 1	Q 10	X 8	U 1	R 1	U 1	D 2	X 8	I 1	G 2	I 1
G 2	S 1	E 1	O 1	E 1	N 1	E 1	B 3	S 1	E 1	V 4	A 1	V 4	L 1
N 1	E 1	Z 10	E 1	M 3	A 1	S 1	C 3	G 2	E 1	E 1	A 1	N 1	L 1
A 1	A 1	U 1	U 1	T 1	I 1	H 4	E 1	R 1	E 1	Z 10	Z 10	J 8	B 3
N 1	C 3	E 1	E 1	D 2	O 1	S 1	S 1	S 1	H 4	X 8	O 1	F 4	O 1
T 1	R 1	R 1	I 1	O 1	I 1	A 1	D 2	G 2	Q 10	S 1	I 1	O 1	A 1
M 3	A 1	N 1	L 1	S 1	L 1	T 1	R 1	A 1	C 3	E 1	S 1	E 1	R 1
A 1	G 2	S 1	F 4	W 4	X 8	K 5	N 1	O 1	Z 10	Z 10	L 1	E 1	Q 10

Word Ladder

Use each of the tiles once to move from the word at the top of the ladder to the word at the bottom. You may only change one letter on each rung of the ladder, and must make a valid word on each rung. Use each of the Scrabble tiles once to do so.

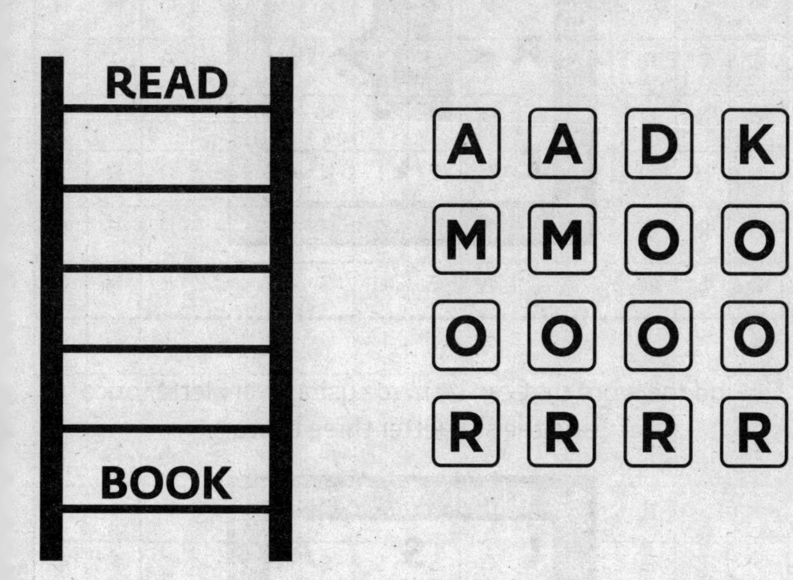

Star Letter

Find the word that can be made using every letter once, and the star letter twice.

....

Find the word that can be made using every letter once, and the star letter three times.

....

Consonant Crossword

Complete the crossword puzzle, in which all the vowels have already been placed. You must use each consonant tile listed once to fill the grid.

Word Splits

Can you combine the word segments
below to make three words?

NOT CON ION AT

....

OBE ENT DI DIS

....

LIG NED EN HTE

....

Link Words

Find the word that can replace the question marks on each line to make two new words or phrases. Use each of the Scrabble tiles once to do so.

COFFEE ????? TENNIS

SNAIL ???? ORDER

FOOT ???? POINT

A A A B
B E I L
L L L M
T

Missing Vowels

All the vowels have been removed from three words. Use each of the vowel tiles below once to reconstruct the words.

1) BLSK

2) BSLN

3) YLDD

A E E E
E E I I
I O

Word Square

Use the Scrabble tiles provided to fill the grid, so that the answer to each crossword clue appears in the corresponding row of the grid. Once complete, the same answer words will also appear in the columns.

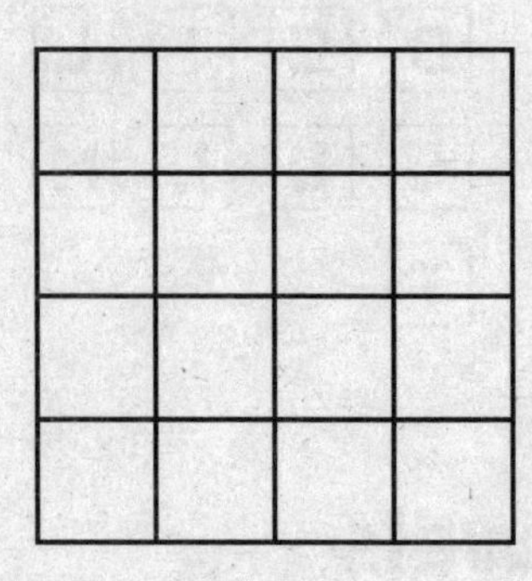

Decapod crustacean

Widespread

From a distance

Mass of floating ice

R R R R

Unscramble

Can you unscramble the two essential oils that have been mixed together below?

BEST MAJOR ENIGMA

....

....

Can you unscramble the three dance styles that have been mixed together below?

BALSA TABLE MURALS

....

....

....

Word Slider

Move each of the sliders up and down in order to form six-letter words in the middle row. Can you find five-or-more words?

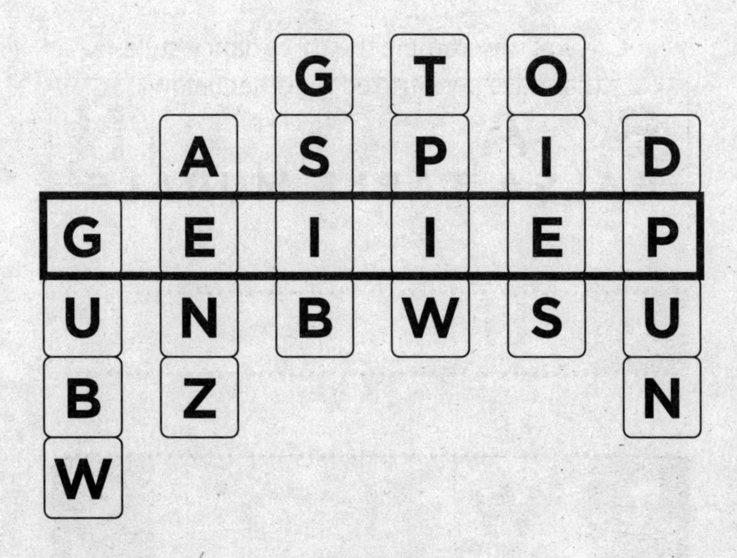

SCRABBLE™ Word

Can you guess the SCRABBLE™ Word? It is a word found in the Scrabble dictionary that does not repeat any letters. In each of the guesses below, a white background means the letter does not appear in the answer word. A black background means a letter is both found in the word and is in the correct position, whilst a grey background means a letter is found in the answer word, but in a different position.

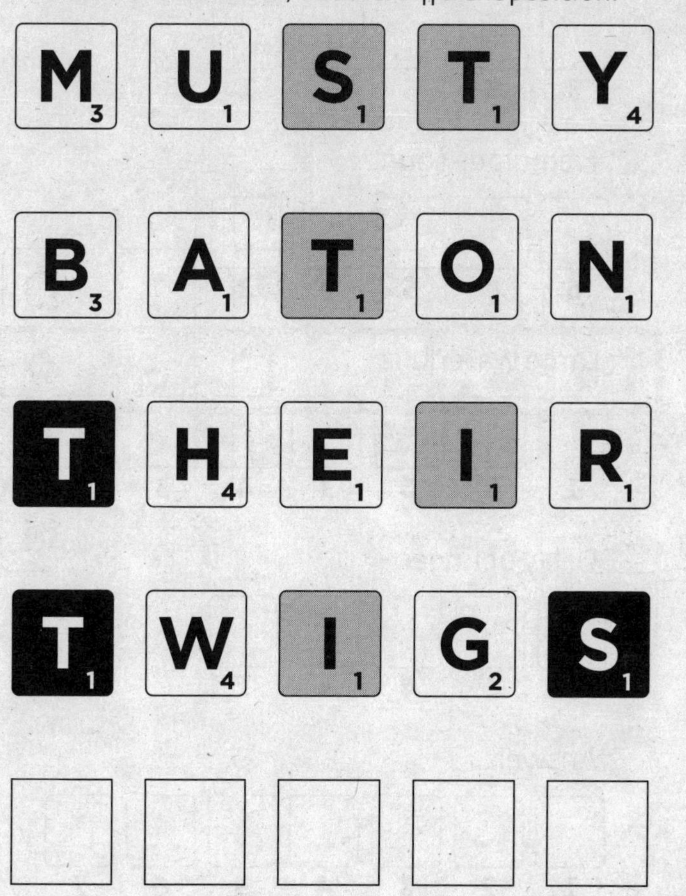

Value of solution tiles: 11 points

Seven Letters

A word composed of seven different letters has been created using Scrabble tiles. Can you answer the clues below to work out what that word is? Numbers indicate the position of each letter in the answer word.

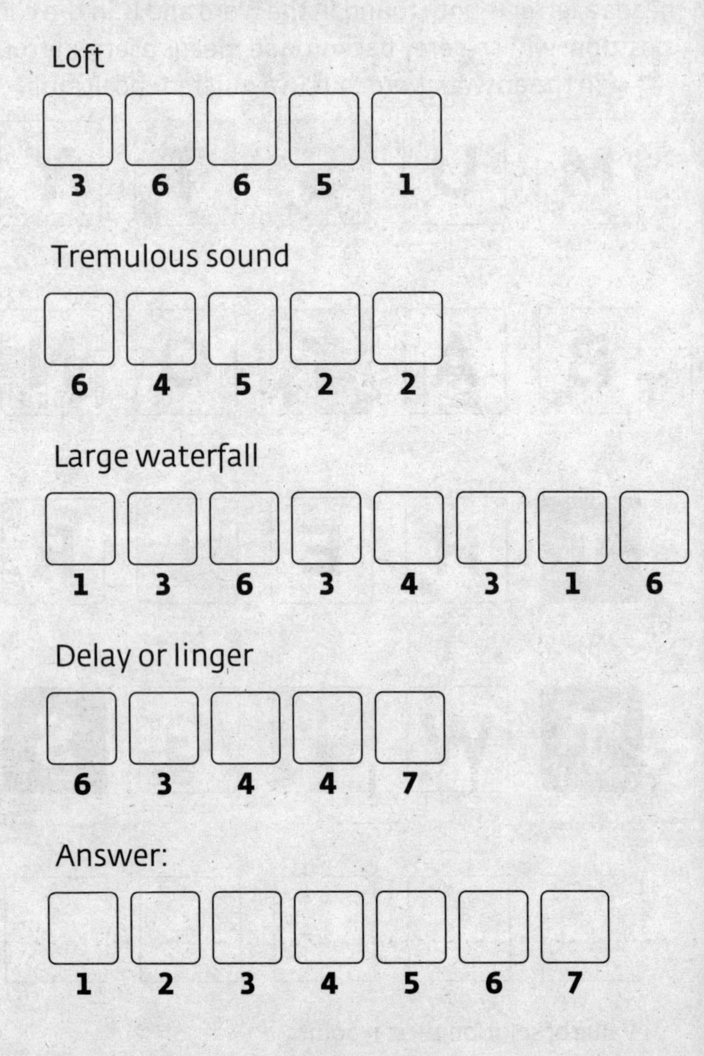

SCRABBLE™ Score

Make the highest score you can from each of the letter racks below. Add 50 points for a seven-letter word.

L1 I1 Y4 L1 G2 E1 N1

T1 G2 E1 A1 N1 T1 N1 — TRIPLE SCORE ON 1ST LETTER

Y4 V4 L1 I1 R1 E1 F4 — TRIPLE WORD SCORE

Wordsearch

Can you find all of these rooms from the Scrabble wordlist in the grid below? Words may appear horizontally, vertically or diagonally in either a forwards or backwards direction.

N	B	Q	C	R	Y	P	T	A	L	C	L	C	L
B	C	Q	M	K	J	E	S	N	E	S	W	X	O
A	L	L	O	O	I	X	J	U	C	T	G	L	U
S	A	V	O	A	O	T	P	A	U	U	B	U	N
E	S	E	S	B	P	R	C	S	Q	D	A	I	G
M	S	W	C	T	B	P	K	H	C	I	T	T	E
E	R	M	I	I	A	Y	E	R	E	O	H	N	M
N	O	O	O	N	F	F	B	G	A	N	R	U	O
T	O	O	T	O	K	F	F	J	V	D	O	R	O
X	M	R	Y	S	R	T	O	R	U	W	O	S	R
G	Y	W	Y	S	T	D	N	G	O	H	M	E	L
Z	L	O	H	V	T	U	E	K	Q	O	V	R	L
Z	R	H	H	A	Z	R	D	B	I	E	M	Y	A
E	U	S	T	L	A	V	G	Y	B	Y	H	T	B

BALLROOM
BASEMENT
BATHROOM
BEDROOM
CLASSROOM
CRYPT
DARKROOM
KITCHEN
LOBBY
LOUNGE
NURSERY
OFFICE
PANTRY
SAUNA
SHOWROOM
STAFFROOM
STUDIO
STUDY

Give Me a Clue

Can you fill-in the blank tiles to create a word
that solves each of the clues below?

Person who provides information

S				C	

Gradual increase in loudness

	R			C				O

Subdivision of an army

B			G			

Difficult to capture

	L				V	

Anagrams

Can you find the word that can be made from the following letters?

QAIUNVSH

....

Can you find the two words that can be made from the following letters?

PDTEORO

....

....

Can you find the three words that can be made from the following letters?

EIRWTH

....

....

....

Themed Anagrams

Can you crack these anagrams of athletics events?

HOT CANDLE

....

LED RUSH

....

CHEAPEST EELS

....

ROMAN HAT

....

Word Wheel

Find as many words of 4+ letters as you can, using the letters in the wheel. All words must use the central letter. One word will use all the letters in the wheel.

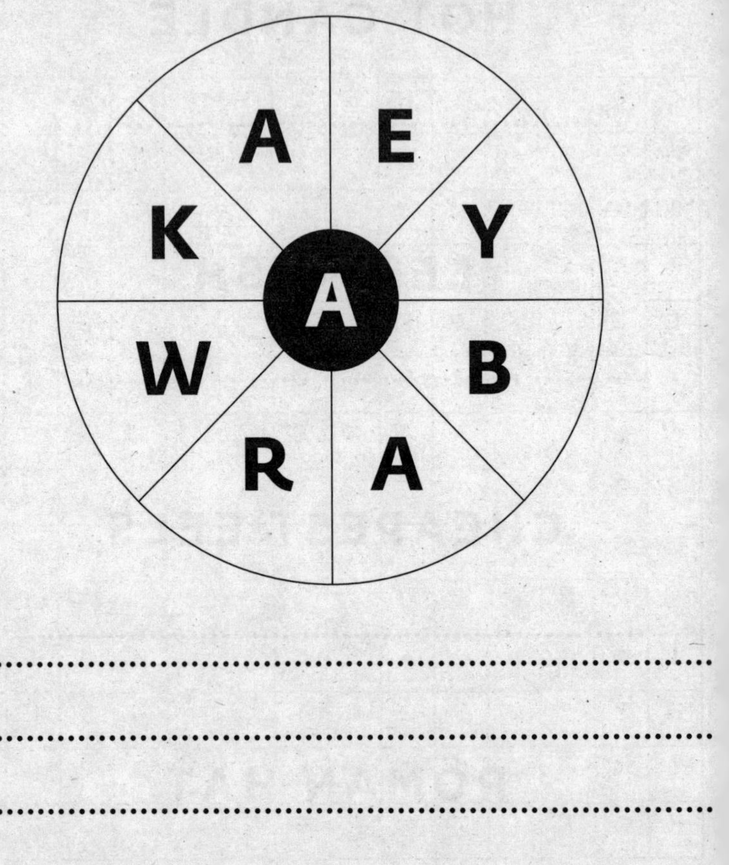

SCRABBLE™ Soup

Find the highest-scoring word you can in the grid of letters below by summing the values assigned to each letter tile in your word: for instance the word EXAMPLE would score 18 points. Words may appear horizontally, vertically or diagonally in the grid, and in either a forwards or backwards direction.

C 3	O 1	A 1	E 1	S 1	H 4	E 1	L 1	V 4	E 1	D 2	L 1	P 3	A 1
N 1	E 1	F 4	A 1	R 1	I 1	O 1	U 1	S 1	X 8	F 4	E 1	F 4	U 1
T 1	W 4	R 1	T 1	M 3	U 1	S 1	C 3	L 1	E 1	G 2	F 4	I 1	T 1
I 1	R 1	E 1	C 3	Y 4	C 3	L 1	E 1	S 1	C 3	I 1	G 2	V 4	K 5
E 1	E 1	F 4	R 1	E 1	K 5	I 1	S 1	E 1	R 1	J 8	O 1	C 3	U 1
I 1	U 1	O 1	F 4	Z 10	H 4	E 1	O 1	M 3	W 4	V 4	O 1	C 3	N 1
W 4	A 1	S 1	P 3	P 3	A 1	H 4	S 1	G 2	S 1	U 1	R 1	B 3	I 1
L 1	B 3	K 5	I 1	T 1	C 3	H 4	E 1	N 1	S 1	L 1	I 1	U 1	V 4
O 1	S 1	E 1	A 1	N 1	C 3	E 1	T 1	I 1	L 1	I 1	N 1	D 2	E 1
L 1	K 5	V 4	E 1	A 1	U 1	E 1	N 1	U 1	O 1	C 3	G 2	G 2	R 1
I 1	A 1	R 1	N 1	Q 10	A 1	Y 4	C 3	F 4	F 4	K 5	E 1	I 1	S 1
H 4	Y 4	A 1	O 1	S 1	Q 10	E 1	I 1	O 1	T 1	E 1	R 1	E 1	E 1
T 1	M 3	G 2	E 1	G 2	N 1	B 3	L 1	U 1	O 1	D 2	E 1	L 1	U 1
H 4	O 1	R 1	A 1	T 1	A 1	R 1	E 1	C 3	A 1	L 1	L 1	E 1	D 2

Word Ladder

Use each of the tiles once to move from the word at the top of the ladder to the word at the bottom. You may only change one letter on each rung of the ladder, and must make a valid word on each rung. Use each of the Scrabble tiles once to do so.

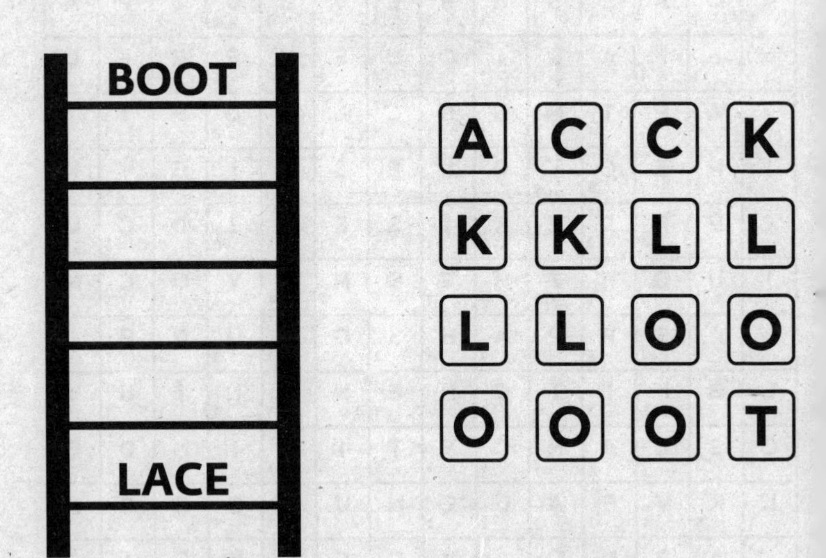

Star Letter

Find the word that can be made using every letter once, and the star letter twice.

....

Find the word that can be made using every letter once, and the star letter three times.

....

Consonant Crossword

Complete the crossword puzzle, in which all the vowels have already been placed. You must use each consonant tile listed once to fill the grid.

Word Splits

Can you combine the word segments below to make three words?

URE EXP DIT EN

....

AM FL NCE YA BO

....

GH WR ER IT OST

....

Link Words

Find the word that can replace the question marks on each line to make two new words or phrases. Use each of the Scrabble tiles once to do so.

SILVER ?????? SAVER

HONEY ???? BEAM

LIME ????? HOUSE

C E E G
H I L M
N N O O
R S T

Missing Vowels

All the vowels have been removed from three words. Use each of the vowel tiles below once to reconstruct the words.

1) MRMB

2) FRTLL

3) QLLY

A A A
E E E
I O U

Word Square

Use the Scrabble tiles provided to fill the grid, so that the answer to each crossword clue appears in the corresponding row of the grid. Once complete, the same answer words will also appear in the columns.

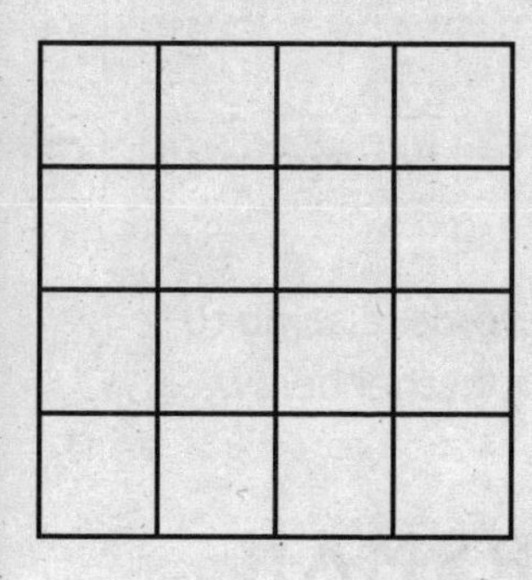

Brag about

Ill-mannered

Lyric poems

Cardinal point

R R S S

T U W W

Unscramble

Can you unscramble the two words that mean 'tired' that have been mixed together below?

GUIDE PET SAFELY

....

....

Can you unscramble the three words relating to physics that have been mixed together below?

TOPMOST OARSMAN

....

....

....

Solutions

Page 6

Words that can be made include:
OILMEN, PACKED, PACKET, PALMED, PICKED, PICKET, SACKED, SICKEN, SILKEN, VALUED

Page 7

HOUSE

Page 8

Answers to clues: COCOON, DODGE, ADAGE,CAGED
Answer: DECAGON

Page 9

1) ABANDON (80)
2) DOCKS (36)
3) KLAXON (22)

Page 10

Page 11

1) DESTROYED
2) WEEVIL
3) BALLAD
4) MARJORAM

Page 12

1) AARDVARK
2) ANNOYED, ANODYNE
3) AIMED, AMIDE, MEDIA

Page 13

1) LIVESTOCK
2) GERMINATION
3) SEEDLING
4) HARVESTING

Page 14

ADULTHOOD

Page 15

HELICOPTERS (18)

Solutions

Page 16

SURF
SURE
SORE
WORE
WOVE
WAVE

Page 17

1) LUMINOSITY
2) CONSIGNMENT

Page 18

Page 19

1) BOUNDARY
2) DIVIDEND
3) BOULEVARD

Page 20

1) TRACK
2) STAFF
3) POOL

1) MACAQUE
2) VISAGE
3) TARRAGON

Page 21

P	A	L	E
A	G	A	R
L	A	V	A
E	R	A	S

Page 22

1) BEAGLE, DACHSHUND
2) LAGOON, STRAIT, BAY

Page 23

Words that can be made include:
CABLED, COILED, DODGED, DOGGED, SAGGED, SAILED, SOILED

Solutions

Page 24
DEITY

Page 25
Answers to clues: GRIEF, GIVER, VERGE, GROVE
Answer: FORGIVE

Page 26
1) PAGEANT (70)
2) SPOOKY (19)
3) VIRTUE (27)

Page 27

Page 28
1) LIMOUSINE
2) BAGGAGE
3) AGENDA
4) DIRECTOR

Page 29
1) BATTERY
2) AUCTION, CAUTION
3) BARELY, BARLEY, BLEARY

Page 30
1) MANUSCRIPT
2) PROVENANCE
3) HISTORIAN
4) CHRONICLE

Page 31
DEBUGGING

Page 32

EJECTION (17)

Page 33
WORK
CORK
COOK
COOP
CHOP
SHOP

Solutions

Page 34

1) EQUIVALENT
2) GHOSTLINESS

Page 35

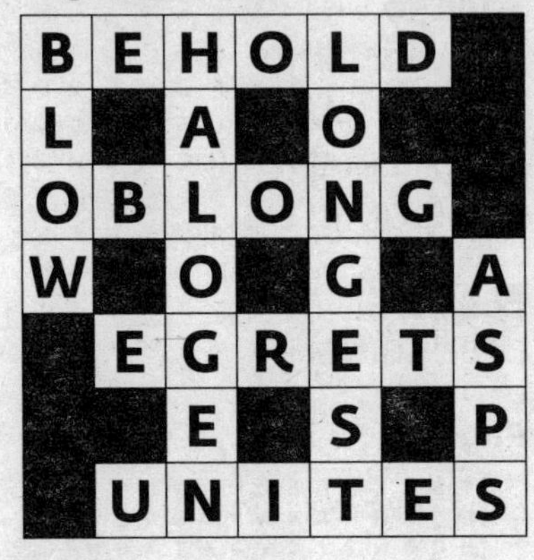

Page 36

1) INDICATE
2) OCCASION
3) PATIENCE

Page 37

1) GRASS
2) SHOW
3) WATCH

1) IRKSOME
2) ILLEGAL
3) ACCUMULATE

Page 38

F	A	R	E
A	M	E	N
R	E	E	D
E	N	D	S

Page 39

1) BROWNIE, TIRAMISU
2) HALIBUT, TUNA, SOLE

Page 40

Words that can be made include: BLAZER, BLAZES, BLOATS, BLOKES, SHAKES, SLAKES

Page 41

NAIVE

Page 42

Answers to clues: TERROR, TREMOR, MUTTER, EGRET
Answer: GOURMET

Solutions

Page 43

1) SYMBOL (15)
2) MAXIM (22)
3) QUENCH (40)

Page 44

Page 45

1) LEAFLET
2) GIMMICK
3) MEDIEVAL
4) BUDGET

Page 46

1) CLEMENCY
2) BELATED, BLEATED
3) COPES, COPSE, SCOPE

Page 47

1) CIRCULATION
2) INFLATION
3) INVESTMENT
4) TRANSACTION

Page 48

VINDICATE

Page 49

SQUABBLES (22)

Page 50

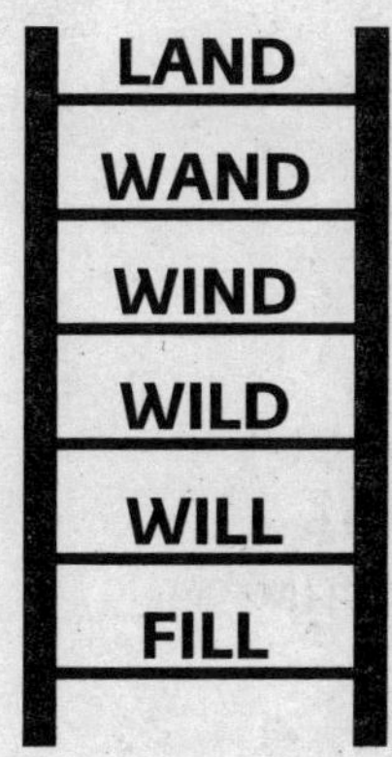

Page 51

1) CHARITABLE
2) REPLACEMENT

Solutions

Page 52

S				F		
C	H	A	R	I	T	Y
H		B		G		O
E	B	B		U	R	N
M		E		R		D
A	U	S	T	E	R	E
		S				R

Page 53

1) PARALLEL
2) SCHEDULE
3) TREASURY

Page 54

1) RACE
2) STATE
3) CHECK

1) ECONOMY
2) CAJOLE
3) CALCIUM

Page 55

A	N	T	S
N	O	R	M
T	R	I	O
S	M	O	G

Page 56

1) FURIOUS, RAGING
2) RAKE, CLAMP, HAMMER

Page 57

Words that can be made include: ACTORS, ALTARS, ALTERS, SAVERS, SAVOUR, SLEEPS, SNEAKS, SNEERS, WATERS, WAVERS

Page 58

ORCAS

Page 59

Answers to clues: RECALL, RULER, RENAL, LEARNER
Answer: UNCLEAR

Solutions

Page 60

1) MARIMBA (76)
2) FRAZZLE (79)
3) NARWHAL (65)

Page 61

Page 62

1) CALENDAR
2) THOROUGH
3) KINETIC
4) SALMON

Page 63

1) DELIGHTED
2) CHARMED, MARCHED
3) DAWDLES, SWADDLE, WADDLES

Page 64

1) ASSIGNMENT
2) COLUMNIST
3) BROADCAST
4) EDITORIAL

Page 65

FLOWERPOT

Page 66

E	A	P	V	Z	B	D	T	M	T	A	U	C	S
P	F	R	K	P	K	I	B	C	U	E	B	F	U
M	R	E	E	H	K	S	O	I	M	S	E	O	I
E	E	L	N	U	T	C	O	B	K	U	E	A	S
M	S	I	C	M	C	R	S	Q	N	T	L	U	N
O	H	M	O	A	E	E	T	I	O	I	E	E	M
R	A	I	D	N	A	D	E	S	B	L	U	A	V
I	U	N	E	I	N	I	R	C	O	I	N	M	Y
A	R	A	S	T	P	T	I	R	D	T	R	O	M
L	W	R	I	Y	D	A	L	Y	I	I	A	U	A
Q	V	Y	G	A	I	B	M	I	E	E	V	R	U
Y	H	R	N	A	J	L	E	N	S	S	E	S	G
C	V	T	S	Z	T	E	I	G	O	F	L	E	W
E	L	E	V	E	R	E	T	B	E	L	I	E	F

DISCREDITABLE (19)

Page 67

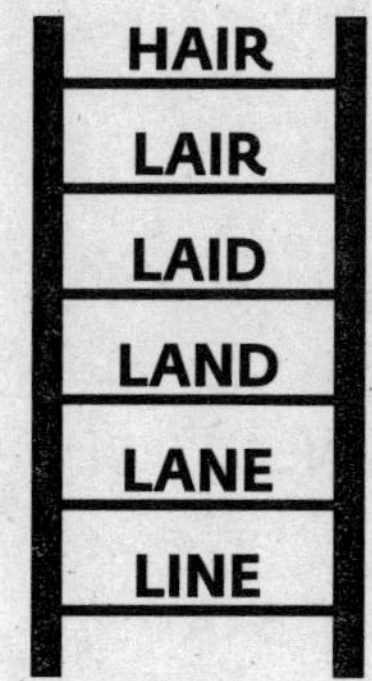

Solutions

Page 68

1) RESPECTFUL
2) VENTURESOME

Page 69

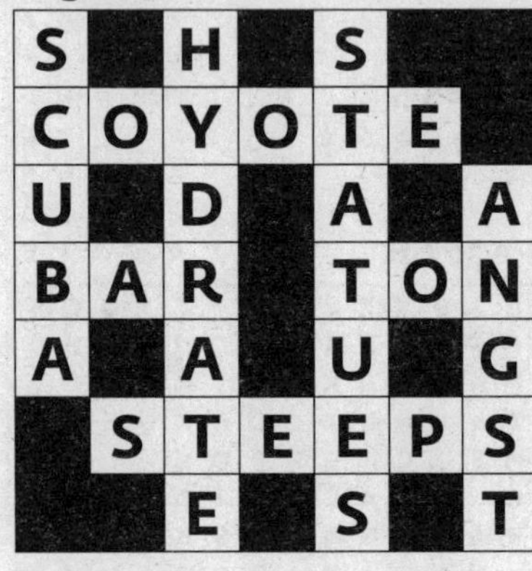

Page 70

1) WEAKNESS
2) ACTIVITY
3) ALLIANCE

Page 71

1) WATER
2) STEP
3) BOARD

1) EQUITY
2) SEESAW
3) GUIDANCE

Page 72

E	W	E	S
W	I	L	T
E	L	S	E
S	T	E	P

Page 73

1) CARNATION, IRIS
2) STAPLE, PENCIL, RULER

Page 74

Words that can be made include: PERMED, PURGED, REAMED, REAPED, SEAMED, SEAMEN, SHAMED, SHAPED, SURGED

Page 75

STUCK

Page 76

Answers to clues: STRATUM, DUSTS, DURUM, MASTS
Answer: MUSTARD

Solutions

Page 77

1) RENEGE (14)
2) UNICORN (77)
3) GATHER (30)

Page 78

H S A T I S F A C T I O N U
O M S V P H Z G M P T Q K E
P C E K T M I K I N W D V Y
E O R Z U N O N E F S O T Q
S U E F Y H E M O S L E N A
I R N S Y T T M E I M R T N
R A I H A N I N E P T H A G
P G T H E D M L A S G A Q E
R E Y T O L N T I I U B L R
U S N J A Y H E L M F M R E
S O C C P Y U E S B U M A J
C H O V P S D Y F S X H S O
H D M B S S E N I P P A H Y
E X C I T E M E N T L A F B

Page 79

1) SALARY
2) VENDETTA
3) CACTUS
4) ENIGMATIC

Page 80

1) EXTROVERT
2) COMPILE, POLEMIC
3) DEARTH, HATRED, THREAD

Page 81

1) UNIVERSE
2) SPACECRAFT
3) SATELLITE
4) ASTEROID

Page 82

PLATITUDE

Page 83

G I R A O G A R I S H K P H
A E D I S T I N C T V E R P
G H O U L I S H W F T E O T
P E N I T E N C E O A R N P
T B L U R B S T T R Y L U R
W N A X P F W P X G O A N E
T U S S O C K S P E R E C S
I O E M D U S P R R U Q I E
B I L L B O A R D L E T A I
U U V A I A U P E C F P T R
P E R T A I N S P S U A I E
I T U B R A I L L E L O O Z
T O C C U P A N T Z T P N O
H Y S T E R I A B R O O M S

PRONUNCIATION (17)

Page 84

Page 85

1) STATIONERY
2) ACHIEVEMENT

Solutions

Page 86

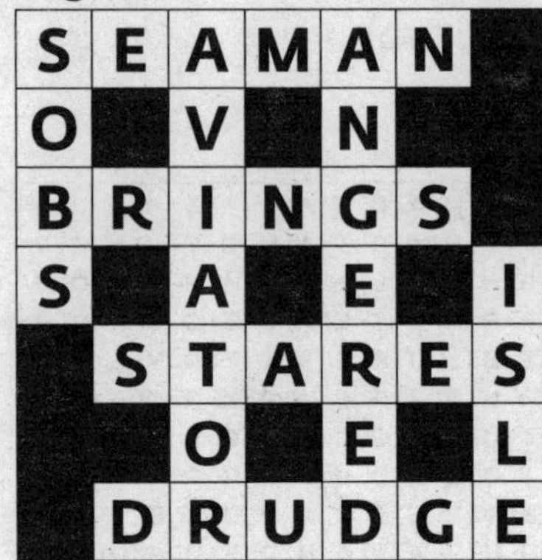

Page 87

1) LATITUDE
2) ACADEMICS
3) APOLOGIES

Page 88

1) PIECE
2) BANK
3) JACK

1) MEADOW
2) ALCOVE
3) ZOOLOGY

Page 89

D	U	E	T
U	N	D	O
E	D	G	Y
T	O	Y	S

Page 90

1) TENNIS, HOCKEY
2) MOPED, BOAT, LORRY

Page 91

Words that can be made include: ANGORA, BLAMED, BLARED, BOLTED, SLATED, SNARED, SOARED

Page 92

JUICY

Page 93

Answers to clues: GROOM, BARBER, GREBE, BARRAGE
Answer: EMBARGO

Solutions

Page 94
1) AURICLE (59)
2) EYEBALL (86)
3) OPULENT (60)

Page 95

Page 96
1) CEVICHE
2) THRILLER
3) CHILDREN
4) VALUABLE

Page 97
1) FLAMINGO
2) FEEDING, FEIGNED
3) DESERTS, DESSERT, TRESSED

Page 98
1) PATTERN
2) EMBOSSING
3) NEEDLEWORK
4) EMBROIDERY

Page 99
TELEPATHY

Page 100

ZOOLOGY (20)

Page 101
SING
SUNG
SUNS
SUES
SUET
DUET

Page 102
1) ASTONISHED
2) DEIFICATION

Solutions

Page 103

Page 104

1) BASICALLY
2) BODYGUARD
3) DEFLECTED

Page 105

1) CHICKEN
2) STAND
3) PIANO

1) RECEIVE
2) CASCADE
3) JAWBONE

Page 106

R	O	A	D
O	G	R	E
A	R	M	S
D	E	S	K

Page 107

1) KNITTING, CROCHET
2) CHICKEN, MOUSE, SHEEP

Page 108

Words that can be made include: LOVING, RAKING, RATING, RAVING, ROVING, WAKING, WAVING

Page 109

BARON

Page 110

Answers to clues: GENRE, RODEO, REIGNED, DENIED
Answer: IGNORED

Solutions

Page 111

1) PLAZA (16)
2) ABLOOM (30)
3) EXPORT (45)

Page 112

Page 113

1) ASPARAGUS
2) VALLEY
3) PIONEER
4) CARAMEL

Page 114

1) GLOSSARY
2) FIENDISH, FINISHED
3) DETAIL, DILATE, TAILED

Page 115

1) ARABESQUE
2) CARTWHEEL
3) SPRINGBOARD
4) SOMERSAULT

Page 116

BAROMETER

Page 117

EXHIBITION (22)

Page 118

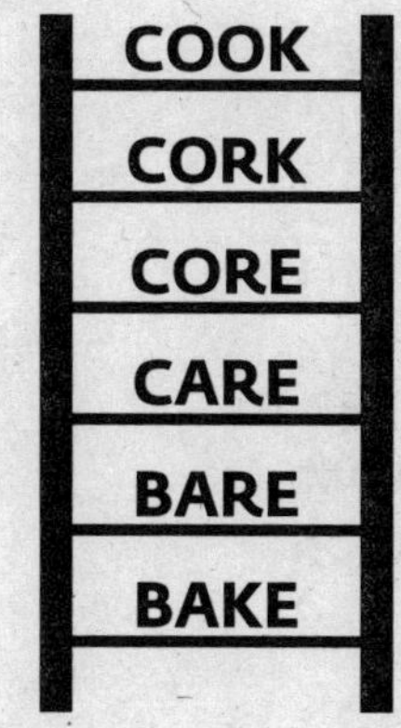

Page 119

1) HORIZONTAL
2) PRESENTABLE

Solutions

Page 120

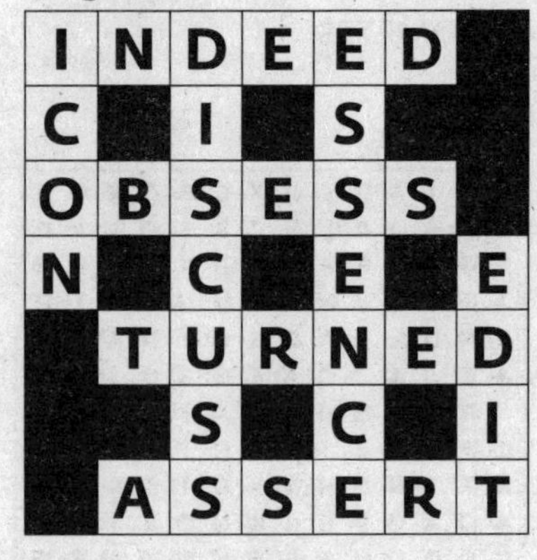

I	N	D	E	E	D	
C		I		S		
O	B	S	E	S	S	
N		C		E		E
	T	U	R	N	E	D
		S		C		I
	A	S	S	E	R	T

Page 121

1) EMULATION
2) FOUNTAINS
3) GUACAMOLE

Page 122

1) TEN
2) FIELD
3) HAMMER

1) ACCELERATE
2) PERFUME
3) VENISON

Page 123

P	O	M	P
O	P	A	L
M	A	M	A
P	L	A	N

Page 124

1) JACKET, TROUSERS
2) TIMER, PAN, GRATER

Page 125

Words that can be made include:
LITTER, LOOSEN, LOOSER, LOOTER, MITTEN, MUTTER, POORER, POTTER, PUTTER

Page 126

EXIST

Page 127

Answers to clues: DODOS, ORATOR, STARED, REARED
Answer: ROASTED

Solutions

Page 128

1) LECTERN (60)
2) PAPYRUS (64)
3) WAYLAY (30)

Page 129

Page 130

MEDICINE
FORTUNE
CAVERNOUS
VOYAGE

Page 131

1) JUBILANT
2) HEPTAGON, PATHOGEN
3) DUSTER, RUDEST, RUSTED

Page 132

1) EARTHENWARE
2) PORCELAIN
3) THROWING
4) CERAMIC

Page 133

UNFOUNDED

Page 134

B	L	E	J	E	S	I	D	E	S	K	T	O	P
U	J	T	A	U	A	P	I	E	U	E	U	W	R
R	G	U	A	N	F	K	A	R	X	I	I	V	S
S	R	U	B	I	E	E	R	E	N	D	E	U	T
A	A	T	S	F	S	L	O	D	I	T	O	V	D
R	N	I	O	I	T	O	O	M	E	E	U	Q	I
I	D	A	L	E	T	O	N	S	U	D	T	V	S
N	M	N	U	S	R	E	Y	T	X	E	R	P	C
G	O	G	T	I	S	H	J	P	R	G	U	O	U
U	T	E	I	S	F	L	B	I	R	R	N	L	S
I	H	L	O	R	G	A	T	Z	U	E	J	L	S
L	E	I	N	U	X	T	F	L	A	E	E	E	E
T	R	C	R	S	H	A	Y	Y	I	S	D	N	Y
Y	P	A	C	O	N	S	I	S	T	E	N	T	F

GRANDMOTHER (18)

Page 135

MONK
MINK
MINT
MIST
FIST
FISH

Page 136

1) DELIGHTFUL
2) HUMILIATION

Solutions

Page 137

Page 138

1) IMPRESSED
2) INTENTION
3) LEGENDARY

Page 139

1) HEAD
2) JUMP
3) PICK

1) GARRISON
2) AIRBAG
3) PENSIVE

Page 140

J	A	R	S
A	G	U	E
R	U	S	T
S	E	T	S

Page 141

1) HURRICANE, THUNDER
2) BASIL, CUMIN, DILL

Page 142

Words that can be made include:
HARASS, HORSES, LARGER, LARGOS, SURFER, SURGES

Page 143

CHILD

Page 144

Answers to clues: DOMINO, DOING, KIMONO, IDIOM
Answer: KINGDOM

Solutions

Page 145

1) ZOMBIE (38)
2) QUILT (34)
3) MILIEU (16)

Page 146

O	E	Z	E	N	O	H	P	O	X	A	S	R	U
M	S	I	L	A	I	T	N	E	T	S	I	X	E
M	E	G	A	P	I	X	E	L	F	R	Q	Y	G
Q	C	Z	C	D	E	T	C	E	P	X	E	N	U
X	O	D	O	H	T	R	O	N	U	X	Y	P	E
G	M	E	E	O	D	W	H	B	P	R	R	X	X
K	P	X	X	X	W	W	E	E	A	E	P	F	T
O	L	A	I	C	D	E	N	I	Y	R	L	O	I
O	E	L	S	T	S	D	L	A	E	E	Q	X	N
B	X	E	T	W	I	I	P	S	X	G	D	H	C
T	I	R	A	T	X	X	S	I	X	G	B	O	T
X	T	X	U	U	A	I	B	J	D	P	B	L	I
E	Y	R	A	T	O	L	Q	E	K	V	R	E	O
T	E	W	O	N	E	X	T	E	R	N	A	L	N

Page 147

1) WARREN
2) LIMESTONE
3) UNIFORM
4) CHARCOAL

Page 148

1) LONGITUDE
2) INTRODUCE, REDUCTION
3) KEELS, LEEKS, SLEEK

Page 149

1) BERYLLIUM
2) FLUORINE
3) PLATINUM
4) STRONTIUM

Page 150

TWITTERED

Page 151

R	O	P	P	R	E	S	S	U	F	M	Y	I	H
B	E	J	I	T	T	E	R	P	R	E	E	E	U
S	W	E	E	T	E	N	E	R	C	L	S	D	V
G	C	U	T	I	C	L	E	D	K	E	P	O	B
B	R	R	R	K	T	O	U	H	L	V	E	W	A
I	V	O	X	B	E	R	P	I	K	A	C	N	S
F	N	I	C	R	O	T	A	T	E	T	I	P	T
O	M	J	S	E	A	D	L	E	X	I	A	L	I
J	R	C	E	C	R	F	I	P	E	O	L	A	O
Q	E	C	R	C	O	I	I	S	R	N	L	Y	N
I	A	R	H	W	T	U	E	A	Y	I	Y	I	L
K	M	U	A	A	O	I	S	S	X	T	R	G	R
I	S	C	Q	T	R	B	O	B	O	S	R	T	E
A	E	R	R	E	O	D	S	N	P	I	Z	U	Y

INJECTION (18)

Page 152

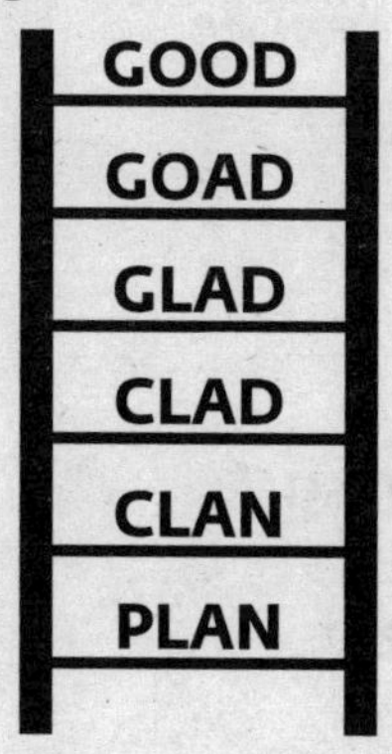

Page 153

1) QUADRANGLE
2) CREDIBILITY

Solutions

Page 154

Page 155

1) WOODPECKER
2) SENSATION
3) TRUTHFULLY

Page 156

1) BACK
2) BOX
3) HAIR

1) TSUNAMI
2) ACOLYTE
3) UPBEAT

Page 157

B	A	T	S
A	U	R	A
T	R	A	P
S	A	P	S

Page 158

1) MAHOGANY, MAPLE
2) STOOL, FUTON, DESK

Page 159

Words that can be made include: FABLED, FAILED, FOILED, PALMED, POLLED, UNITED, UNKIND

Page 160

THICK

Page 161

Answers to clues: MAMBA, IMAGINE, BINGE, MAGMA.
Answer: BEAMING

Solutions

Page 162

1) RAVIOLI (60)
2) HOLDING (64)
3) ACTUARY (62)

Page 163

I	L	C	Q	J	L	Y	G	J	O	R	K	Y	C
A	M	E	T	H	Y	S	T	P	W	U	L	M	W
S	C	E	Z	H	S	W	A	Q	V	B	S	T	A
H	R	M	N	B	K	L	A	K	J	Y	S	X	S
X	E	E	D	I	Q	N	A	I	D	I	S	B	O
E	Y	T	N	I	R	J	Z	L	J	A	D	E	R
T	R	N	I	O	A	A	Z	T	R	A	U	Q	Z
O	J	I	O	H	T	M	M	B	J	A	U	Z	F
D	E	A	H	K	C	S	O	A	I	W	E	B	D
I	F	A	S	P	Z	A	N	N	U	Y	A	P	T
R	V	D	W	P	P	W	L	U	D	Q	X	T	O
E	Z	F	D	X	E	A	N	A	S	Y	A	P	P
P	A	M	B	E	R	R	S	V	M	L	J	G	A
R	M	L	E	N	I	P	S	W	G	J	X	Q	Z

Page 164

1) SCHEME
2) GAZPACHO
3) MARZIPAN
4) TORNADO

Page 165

1) MODERATE
2) LATTICE, TACTILE
3) KILNS, LINKS, SLINK

Page 166

1) LIPSTICK
2) CONCEALER
3) EYESHADOW
4) PRIMER

Page 167

BIOGRAPHY

Page 168

T	A	D	V	E	N	T	U	R	E	T	L	K	T
W	E	E	X	T	E	N	T	S	X	I	E	S	A
G	C	Q	E	U	F	L	G	E	N	C	I	A	A
A	O	Q	I	W	T	E	M	N	T	L	N	T	R
R	L	E	G	A	H	A	E	S	I	E	C	M	S
I	L	M	G	C	R	T	B	R	S	S	I	O	I
S	I	X	B	E	I	R	I	J	E	K	T	S	S
H	E	W	I	Y	C	O	R	U	R	S	I	P	T
A	C	S	X	K	E	T	I	E	P	A	N	H	E
U	N	F	O	U	N	D	E	D	E	R	G	E	R
M	A	G	N	E	T	I	C	F	N	O	H	R	H
S	T	U	D	I	E	S	S	Y	T	N	S	I	O
F	R	U	E	U	D	N	K	H	S	G	T	C	O
A	A	P	P	O	I	N	T	M	E	N	T	H	D

ATMOSPHERIC (20)

Page 169

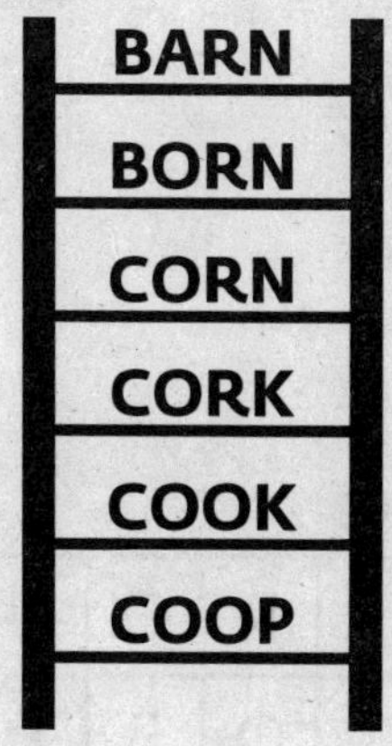

Page 170

1) OBLIGATORY
2) MASTERPIECE

Solutions

Page 171

Page 172

1) TRANSCRIBE
2) SYNONYMOUS
3) LANDSCAPED

Page 173

1) BOOK
2) BAND
3) POST

1) COHESIVE
2) UPHEAVAL
3) ATOMIC

Page 174

I	R	O	N
R	O	B	E
O	B	O	E
N	E	E	D

Page 175

1) CRICKET, APHID
2) BRAIN, HEART, LUNG

Page 176

Words that can be made include: BAKING, BASHES, BASING, BASINS, BIKING, EASING, PAVING

Page 177

UNCLE

Page 178

Answers to clues: RECAP, ICICLE, LILAC, CLEARER
Answer: REPLICA

Page 179

DRINKS (33)
JUMPER (17)
ZEALOUS (67)

Page 180

Solutions

Page 181

1) AMATEUR
2) RECORD
3) PATIENT
4) LEXICON

Page 182

1) PERTINENT
2) ORGANIST, ROASTING
3) OBSERVE, OBVERSE, VERBOSE

Page 183

1) CROCODILE
2) TORTOISE
3) PORCUPINE
4) MARMOSET

Page 184

LEVITATED

Page 185

E H J F U Q W G E Q O E S T
M A Q L R A U G O R I L L A
X M P A B S T A I N E D A A
U S I V V A I L U P C H W N
L T C O N C E P T N U E D N
A E P L U M E D V U T P E U
N R L J I A N C H O R S A L
D M I L L I O N L P N S L M
E C O R D I A L A E N D I E
D A L T S B I O J A W B N N
K R [R O A D B L O C K] N G T
E J R A T D E S I C C A T E
E S Q U A L L O Z I U P C A
E Y R O R R E S E N T F U L

ROADBLOCK (18)

Page 186

Page 187

CAMPAIGNER
RESPECTABLE

Page 188

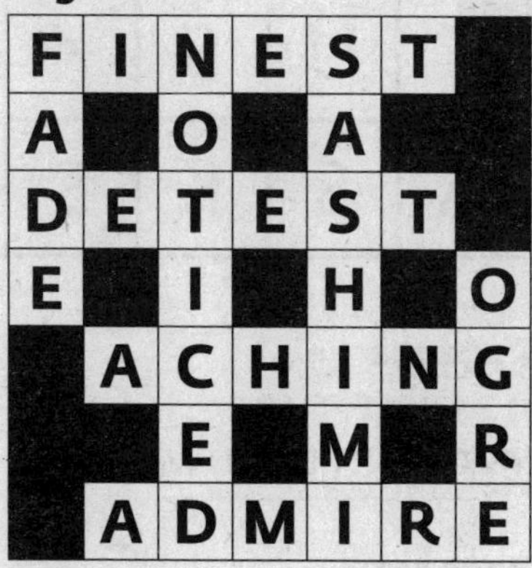

Page 189

1) RHETORICAL
2) PROCEDURAL
3) PRESCIENCE

Solutions

Page 190

1) CRACK
2) STAR
3) SHIP

1) SOMEHOW
2) EARWIG
3) NOWHERE

Page 191

I	O	T	A
O	N	U	S
T	U	S	K
A	S	K	S

Page 192

1) BANGLE, TIARA
2) ACORN, PECAN, WALNUT

Page 193

Words that can be made include: DEEPER, DENIER, DIPPER, TINIER, TIPPER, VENEER, VIEWER

Page 194

CLEAR

Page 195

Answers to clues: FILLY, FLAIL, FAMILY, APPLY
Answer: AMPLIFY

Page 196

1) SQUAWK (42)
2) TEXTILE (64)
3) LANTERN (71)

Page 197

H	T	T	K	B	M	M	L	H	A	D	B	M	A
G	Z	N	B	U	N	V	L	I	T	N	T	N	E
K	Q	M	D	R	R	T	I	B	Y	R	F	S	J
S	A	Y	N	D	O	C	D	I	T	E	O	P	F
S	N	X	O	O	H	N	O	S	W	R	S	S	V
O	O	C	M	C	T	E	T	C	Z	G	K	A	T
B	M	E	L	K	W	T	V	U	O	C	B	G	C
I	A	W	A	Z	A	T	A	S	A	N	F	E	G
O	N	P	H	Z	H	L	Z	R	N	E	U	I	L
O	N	A	G	U	P	E	D	M	N	E	N	T	I
R	I	P	A	U	K	A	H	N	D	S	L	I	M
B	C	A	W	L	M	W	E	Q	E	G	L	V	E
P	S	Y	D	O	M	L	L	N	E	L	P	P	A
M	F	A	M	G	I	N	G	E	R	S	I	C	W

Page 198

1) CLIENT
2) STRATEGY
3) BLIZZARD
4) PATENT

Solutions

Page 199

1) SANDWICH
2) PRESUME, SUPREME
3) OVERT, TROVE, VOTER

Page 200

1) HEADLAMP
2) WILDERNESS
3) FOOTWEAR
4) ENVIRONMENT

Page 201

HUNDREDTH

Page 202

GRAPHICS (16)

Page 203

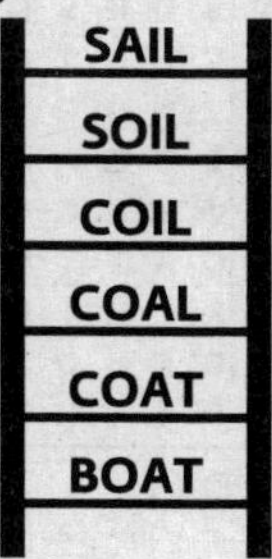

Page 204

1) SEPARATING
2) CIRCUMSPECT

Page 205

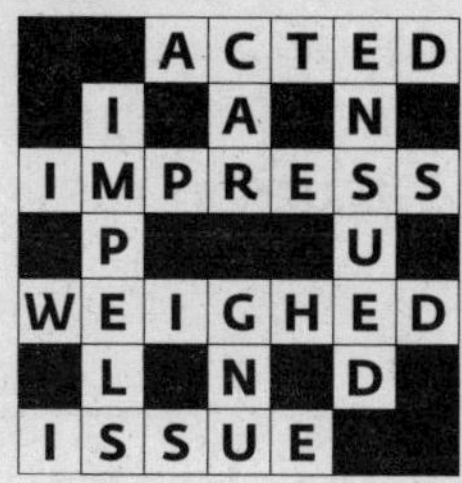

Page 206

1) ITERATION
2) NEGLIGENCE
3) NARRATIVES

Page 207

1) BAG
2) CASE
3) DROP

1) HEROIC
2) VAGUELY
3) MEDIATE

Page 208

B	R	A	G
R	A	T	E
A	T	O	M
G	E	M	S

Solutions

Page 209

1) APRICOT, MANGO
2) BAT, MOLE, PUMA

Page 210

Words that can be made include: CEASES, CURSES, CURVES, JERSEY, JURIES, TEASES, TURRET

Page 211

BASIL

Page 212

Answers to clues: MARRY, MIDDAY, DADDY, IMPAIR
Answer: PYRAMID

Page 213

1) ANDROID (68)
2) BREACH (17)
3) GARLAND (59)

Page 214

H	L	E	Y	I	P	O	E	T	R	Y	D	F	C
M	E	R	R	J	D	F	I	C	T	I	O	N	P
N	V	U	D	T	R	S	R	W	H	O	X	Q	G
V	O	T	X	P	U	R	M	V	V	Y	N	L	N
X	N	A	Z	L	E	N	E	C	S	E	O	E	I
S	W	R	J	O	R	O	H	T	U	A	P	C	T
N	D	E	F	T	U	S	X	P	U	Z	X	A	T
N	I	T	C	H	A	R	A	C	T	E	R	P	E
T	A	I	W	P	P	E	M	L	Z	C	U	S	S
I	L	L	A	L	L	R	I	O	M	E	M	L	Q
C	O	H	A	Y	U	Q	G	Z	Z	O	L	P	S
H	G	Y	T	D	Z	W	W	B	D	R	A	M	A
G	U	S	X	A	C	T	I	O	N	T	E	K	V
S	E	I	E	S	U	S	P	E	N	S	E	C	L

Page 215

1) MACAQUE
2) FOXTROT
3) HARDWARE
4) GARLAND

Page 216

1) SUPERNOVA
2) ROYALIST, SOLITARY
3) SERVES, SEVERS, VERSES

Page 217

1) ARTICHOKE
2) CAULIFLOWER
3) PARSNIP
4) SPINACH

Page 218

ACCORDION

Page 219

W	E	E	D	E	D	P	J	A	C	G	V	A	S
J	E	R	D	E	N	R	I	X	O	R	C	A	T
B	O	I	C	R	P	O	A	U	M	K	O	R	R
U	P	R	O	L	I	V	R	A	P	N	N	T	O
N	N	I	I	W	U	I	D	B	A	U	V	W	N
D	A	N	N	R	B	D	R	S	R	T	I	O	G
R	J	H	C	A	U	E	O	T	E	M	N	R	H
E	E	U	I	T	Z	N	U	R	S	E	C	K	O
S	S	M	D	H	Z	T	G	A	R	G	I	V	L
S	T	A	E	F	W	I	H	C	S	W	N	A	D
T	E	N	N	U	O	A	T	T	M	T	G	E	A
H	R	I	T	L	R	L	E	I	R	O	L	L	P
R	S	T	S	R	D	F	L	O	E	O	Y	K	T
S	A	Y	U	J	P	B	L	N	D	I	S	O	E

BUZZWORD (32)

Solutions

Page 220

WISH
WISE
WIRE
WORE
BORE
BONE

Page 221

1) UNIVERSITY
2) EXCEEDINGLY

Page 222

Page 223

1) ANNIVERSARY
2) TURNSTILE
3) COMPARATIVE

Page 224

1) CHART
2) CHAIR
3) GREEN

1) TOBACCO
2) WARFARE
3) LOGBOOK

Page 225

Z	I	N	G
I	D	E	A
N	E	W	T
G	A	T	E

Page 226

1) ORANGE, PURPLE
2) SLATE, CHALK, SHALE

Page 227

Words that can be made include:
PIPITS, PIPPED, PITIED,
PITIES, SIPPED, TIPPED,
TITHED, TITHES

Page 228

FARCE

Page 229

Answers to clues: ARCANE,
INANE, NICER, ITERATE
Answer: CERTAIN

Page 230

1) OCCUR (27)
2) BREWERY (95)
3) OSPREY (11)

Solutions

Page 231

Page 232

1) BOUTIQUE
2) BUNGALOW
3) PORTRAIT
4) ROBUST

Page 233

1) TRUMPET
2) STATEMENT, TESTAMENT
3) SKATED, STAKED, TASKED

Page 234

1) MIGRATION
2) DISCOVERY
3) EXPLORATION
4) AEROPLANE

Page 235

LIGHTENED

Page 236

NOZZLE (24)

Page 237

READ
ROAD
ROAM
ROOM
ROOK
BOOK

Page 238

1) PERSONALLY
2) RESEMBLANCE

Page 239

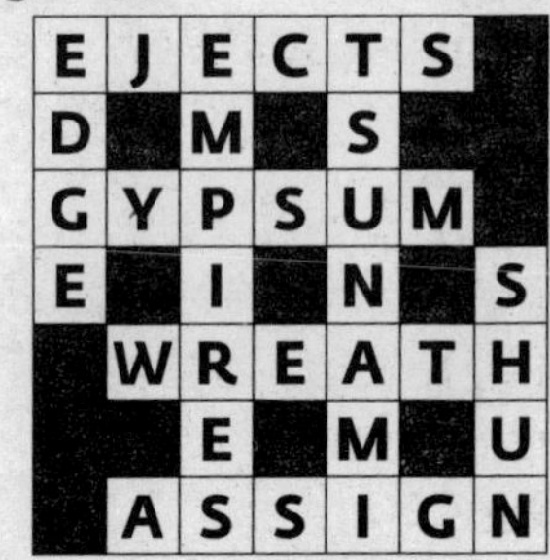

Solutions

Page 240
1) CONNOTATION
2) DISOBEDIENT
3) ENLIGHTENED

Page 241
1) TABLE
2) MAIL
3) BALL

1) OBELISK
2) BASELINE
3) YIELDED

Page 242

C	R	A	B
R	I	F	E
A	F	A	R
B	E	R	G

Page 243
1) BERGAMOT, JASMINE
2) BALLET, SALSA, RUMBA

Page 244
Words that can be made include: BAITED, BASTED, BESTED, GASPED, UNITED, WAITED, WASTED

Page 245
TICKS

Page 246
Answers to clues: ATTIC, TRILL, CATARACT, TARRY
Answer: CLARITY

Page 247
1) YELLING (61)
2) TANGENT (60)
3) VERIFY (45)

Page 248

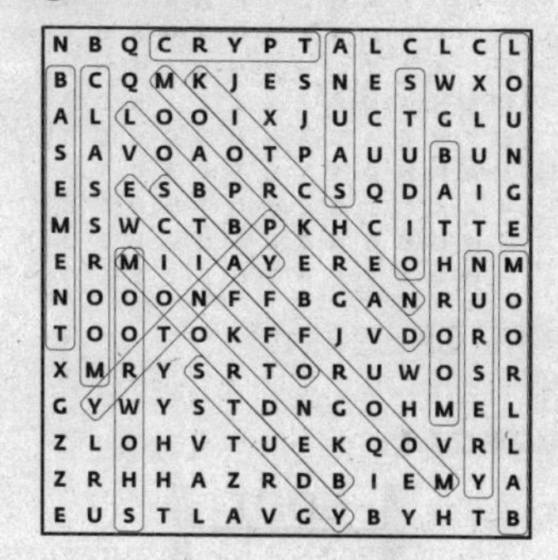

Page 249
1) SOURCE
2) CRESCENDO
3) BRIGADE
4) ELUSIVE

Page 250
1) VANQUISH
2) TORPEDO, TROOPED
3) WHITER, WITHER, WRITHE

Solutions

Page 251
1) DECATHLON
2) HURDLES
3) STEEPLECHASE
4) MARATHON

Page 252
BREAKAWAY

Page 253

KITCHENS (17)

Page 254

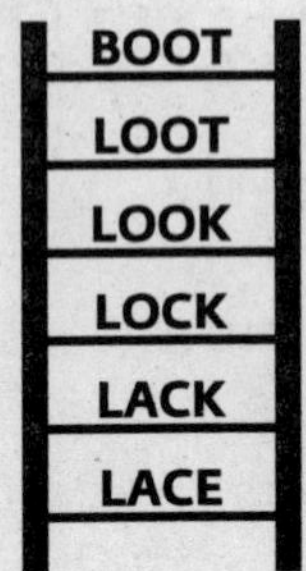

Page 255
1) FREQUENTLY
2) DEFERENTIAL

Page 256

Page 257
1) EXPENDITURE
2) FLAMBOYANCE
3) GHOSTWRITER

Page 258
1) SCREEN
2) MOON
3) LIGHT

1) MARIMBA
2) FORETELL
3) EQUALLY

Page 259

C	R	O	W
R	U	D	E
O	D	E	S
W	E	S	T

Page 260
1) FATIGUED, SLEEPY
2) ATOM, PROTON, MASS